Best Wishes,

Frank Turned

Maunsell – The Firm and Its Founder

Guy Anson Maunsell

(1884-1961)

Maunsell
The Firm and Its Founder

Nigel Watson & Frank Turner

Privately published in 2005
by AECOM Technology Corporation

ISBN-13: 978-0-9552196-0-3
ISBN-10: 0-9552196-0-4

Printed in China through Colorcraft Ltd., Hong Kong

Contents

Foreword
by Sir Wilfred Newton

I am delighted to write this foreword for the 50th anniversary of the formation of G Maunsell & Partners which became one of the world's more distinguished civil engineering consultancies.

Founded in 1955 by Guy Anson Maunsell, an outstanding, far-seeing engineer, innovator and inspiration to his colleagues, the partnership grew to become an integrated group of companies, built on a sound foundation of first-class engineering, environmental responsibility and thorough professionalism. From its British origins it became a genuinely global force in civil engineering consultancy. This was no accidental, haphazard process; it was a considered development, managed with patience and determination, seizing opportunities, benefiting from a succession of talented engineers and managers in many countries on several continents. As with all successful business ventures, it suffered at times from difficulties born of adverse economic circumstances and of internal differences; it also capitalised on benign circumstances at other times.

While sometimes more focused on serving clients and carrying out projects than on commercial success, the firm, under a succession of leaders, has retained Guy Maunsell's guiding principles. The interdependence and mutual support within the Maunsell family worldwide has remained one of its key strengths as the group has moved towards a more unified structure.

I am sure Guy Maunsell would be delighted to see the consultancy he led and founded through its first formative years in its present guise as Maunsell AECOM. The firm continues to spread its expertise even further from its well-established areas of activity, such as the European Union, the Middle East, Australasia, Hong Kong and the Far East, into North America and China, the world's current boom continent.

The story to date is one of compelling interest but it is certainly not the end of the Maunsell history.

Sir Wilfred Newton, CBE
Autumn 2005

Acknowledgements

The preparation of this short life of Guy Maunsell and the firm he founded could not have been compiled without the kind and generous help and advice the author has received from many other people.

Firstly, Shakir Al-Kubaisi was a generous host and gave invaluable guidance to the author in his research, together with his colleagues on the editorial board, Tony Herbert, Richard Garrett and Richard Hankin. It was thanks to Shakir's foresight and initiative some 20 years ago that an archive of material was available today for this book.

Secondly, the material on Guy Maunsell is derived almost entirely from the research and generous assistance of Frank Turner. He has been pursuing almost single-handedly a campaign over the last few years to promote the work and reputation of this extraordinary and under-recognised civil engineer, and his invaluable contribution is an integral part of this book.

The text has been greatly enriched through the use of contributions made in interviews with numerous members of the firm from around the world. I would like to thank in particular, in addition to those already mentioned, Paul Andrew, Francis Bong, John Downer, Leslie Ellis, Geoff Fernie, Peter Gray, Peter Head, David Hook, Peter Johnson, John Laurie, Jim Leslie, David Maher, David Odgers, Ed Plewa, John Read, Nigel Robinson, Pat Sands, Tony Shum, Michael Worrall and Marion West. I have also appreciated the written contributions received from several of the above together with Peter Harris and Roger Wright.

This book could not have been produced without the generous financial support of AECOM, Maunsell in Australia and Hong Kong, and Faber-Maunsell in the UK.

A business like Maunsell is built through the contribution of staff at every level within the organisation. While there are references to several people in the text, the reader should not assume that their contribution to the company's success outweighs the invaluable service given by so many whose names cannot be mentioned because of lack of space. The story recounted in this book is a tribute to all those who have worked for Maunsell over the years. Each of them has played their own part in making it the international success it is today.

Nigel Watson
Autumn 2005

Introduction

This is the story of one man, Guy Maunsell, and the firm he founded. It is also the story of the engineers he employed and all those who have made the firm what it is today. They have all believed they were part of something special and, through commitment, personal integrity and technical excellence, the firm became a giant of the engineering world. Today, as part of the AECOM Group, Maunsell belongs to the largest consulting engineering group in the world.

In 2005 the firm celebrated 50 years of remarkable achievement since its foundation. But the story starts before 1955. Guy Maunsell's own career, spanning two world wars and the depression which separated them, owed in turn a debt to the great Victorian engineers who had preceded him.

Engineers have always been society's unsung heroes yet they have played a pivotal role in the success of civilisation. The engineer has always created the structures and infrastructure needed by society. The earliest engineering structures were probably military, such as the prehistoric hill forts of Britain and the Great Wall of China. There were also other great early achievements, such as China's Grand Canal, the pyramids of Egypt and Central and South America and the roads and aqueducts created by the Romans. Engineers were responsible for the infrastructure that supported society in times of peace, the roads and aqueducts, ports and canals, drains and sewers.

As this aspect of engineering became more marked during the eighteenth century, particularly with the advent of the industrial revolution, engineers adopted the term 'civil' to distinguish them from military engineers. In Britain, the first man to describe himself as a civil engineer was John Smeaton, the builder of the Eddystone lighthouse. Today, when the profession is divided into so many specialities, from mechanical and electrical engineering to aeronautical and marine engineering, the description has become less distinctive.

Nevertheless, the definition of civil engineering given in 1828 by Thomas Tredgold, the British architect and engineer, still holds true today, even though the language has changed. His words, included in the charter of incorporation of the Institution of Civil Engineers, define civil engineering as

> *the art of directing the Great Sources of Power in Nature for the use and convenience of man, being that practical application of the most important principles of natural philosophy which has, in a considerable degree ... changed the aspect and state of affairs in the whole world. The most important object of Civil Engineering is to improve the means of production and of traffic in states, both for external and internal trade.*

That statement has inspired generations of young engineers. It encapsulates the important part which engineering plays in a society's economy. Today we can recognise the disadvantage that an incomplete infrastructure imposes upon the economies of developing countries. The examples of Hong Kong in the late twentieth century and China in the early twenty-first century clearly demonstrate the enormous benefits which can accrue from infrastructure investment.

The development of the profession was spurred on during the industrial revolution through the work of the great British engineers, such as Telford and McAdam, Brindley and Rennie, Stephenson, Locke and Brunel. The advent of the railways stimulated new ideas, new materials, new ways of doing things. It produced the first great contractors and, in the partnership of Joseph Locke and Thomas Brassey, the combination of an engineer with a professional approach to contracts and a contractor of equal technical ability whom the engineer might trust implicitly. This mutual respect between engineer and contractor was an approach that Guy Maunsell would champion throughout his life. His down-to-earth attitude to personal relations not only created a friendly atmosphere for staff, it also produced a more relaxed relationship between clients and contractors. Within the firm there was always a desire to communicate and work as a team, never an arrogance which dismissed another's point of view out of hand. As a result, the firm benefited from repeat work from clients and contractors who appreciated this.

Locke and Brassey built railways all over Europe. Their peers and those who followed them exported British engineering expertise for the benefit of countries all over the world. This tradition of transferring knowledge to other countries, of recruiting and training local engineers, was also an example which Maunsell and his firm would follow to the present day.

Guy Maunsell also admired the practical application of new ideas that marks out the greatest engineers. Another talented British engineer of the early nineteenth century, H R Palmer, succinctly summed this up in 1818 when he wrote that

an engineer is a mediator between the philosopher and the working mechanic, and,
like an interpreter between two foreigners, must understand the language of both ... Hence
the absolute necessity of his possessing both practical and theoretical knowledge.

This was a principle in which Guy believed passionately. A strong character with immense confidence in his own judgement, he fought hard to persuade others of the validity of his own ideas, often implementing them in the face of tough opposition. This would be another key to the success of the firm.

The chapters which follow tell the story of Maunsell and the firm he founded. He was known within the profession as a 'giant in engineering' and 'a very brilliant civil engineer'. He excelled in transportation engineering and the design of bridges. There were even those who called him a genius. But, unlike the great engineers of the Victorian era, he is hardly remembered today. He never received any awards, he never became president of any of the professional bodies, and he never bothered whether he had any publicity or none. Yet he made a vital engineering contribution to the United Kingdom during the Second World War, he pioneered the use of prestressed concrete, and the best of his designs, such as the bridges built after the war in Australia, are regarded as modern classics. He deserves to be more widely recognised.

It is a story of setbacks as well as successes, of persistence and determination which over time created a firm with several thousand staff working all over the world. It shows how the firm, while retaining the key characteristics of its founder, grew through accepting change and adapting to new challenges. Above all, it highlights the continuous contribution made by the firm around the globe in providing the infrastructure needed by modern society. Today, as the scale of those needs continues to expand, it is more important than ever that good engineers find appropriate solutions to meet them. Perhaps the story of Guy Maunsell and his firm will inspire them to do that.

Guy Anson Maunsell

(1884-1961)

Part 1
1884-1955

The Early Life of
Guy Anson Maunsell – 1884-1914

Guy Maunsell was born on 1 September 1884 in Srinagar in Kashmir where his father, Lieutenant-Colonel Edward Maunsell, was serving with the Indian Army. By all accounts, Edward Maunsell was a rather severe man, an Irish Protestant with little interest in anything other than the men and horses under his command. Guy's mother, Rosalie, came from a Staffordshire family and had married Edward in Bombay Cathedral in 1878. Guy had two sisters, Muriel, who died in infancy, and Olive, who later married a South African engineer and made her home in Durban.

The Maunsells were a well-known family in Limerick in Ireland. The family name came from Le Mans in northern France where an inhabitant was known as a 'mansel'. The family arrived in the English county of Buckinghamshire sometime after the Norman Conquest in 1066. Walter Maunsell is recorded as living there in 1166. Captain Thomas Maunsell, who had served in the fleet that defeated the Spanish Armada in 1588, moved to Ireland in 1609 where the family finally settled in Limerick. At the time of Guy's birth, Limerick was still part of the United Kingdom.

Born in India of Irish descent, the partition of Ireland and the end of Empire gave Guy some concern about his nationality in later life as he travelled more widely. Was he Irish, Indian or British? The then principal of the passport office, Miss Williams, who knew his secretary, the redoubtable Mrs Patterson, assured him his British nationality was secure as long as his father was himself British. But in his most recent application Guy had inserted Limerick as his father's birthplace. Miss Williams located the previous application, discovered the entry showed the English town of Bedford as the birthplace, and herself crossed out Limerick and entered Bedford instead – thus, she pointed out, avoiding Guy the embarrassment of applying for British nationality

Like many sons of the Raj, Guy was sent back to England for his education and attended Eastbourne College on the south coast. He was an able pupil and his daughter Maureen later recalled that 'on one occasion he won so many prizes that a fag [a junior pupil assigned to carry out menial tasks for senior boys] had to be called to carry the books away'.

Although it would have been natural for Guy to follow his father into the army, he had always wanted to be a civil engineer. There was only a hint in his family history which might have suggested this as a future career. One of his distant and more distinguished relations, General Sir Frederick Maunsell, who flourished during the second half of the nineteenth century and whom Guy may have known, spent part of his military career in the Royal Engineers.

The nineteenth century was a golden age for civil engineering. Many of the great Victorian engineers are still household names today. Their achievements were still fresh in the memory when Guy Maunsell was growing up. Their exploits would have been glorified in his childhood reading. Civil engineering was exciting, full of challenges, worthwhile. It also received official encouragement as part of the drive to maintain Britain's technical leadership over rivals such as Germany during the late nineteenth and early twentieth centuries. Standards were rising as professional education expanded. When it came to a choice for Guy between a career in the army and one in civil engineering, there was no competition.

He studied at the Central Institution of the City & Guilds Institute in South Kensington in London. The Institute was part of the campaign to revive technical education in the UK. Founded in 1878, the Institute opened the doors of the Central Institution in the year Guy Maunsell was born. He was among the top graduates of his year, passing his examinations with first class honours. Yet despite his qualifications, this intelligent, knowledgeable young engineer was unable to find a job. Instead, he travelled around the country, capturing the scenes of his wanderings with sketch pad and watercolour paints.

He returned to the Central Institution in 1906 where he spent two years employed as a technical demonstrator, setting up experiments for the students. Then, in 1907, at the age of 23, he became an assistant engineer for the firm of Adrien Palaz in the Swiss city of Lausanne, working on hydroelectric installations in France and Switzerland. In 1908 he returned to the UK as the agent for the contracting firm of D G Somerville & Co, handling ferro-concrete and structural steel contracts.

Concrete, successfully developed on a commercial scale by the British and the French in the early nineteenth century, was in common use by the 1880s. By then steel, thanks to the mass production made possible by the Bessemer converter, was relatively cheap. This led to the re-discovery by a Frenchman, Monier, of reinforced concrete, which had been known previously to the Greeks and would become one of the most common of building materials. It was increasingly being used in Britain, for electricity generating stations, for hydro-electric schemes, for the cladding of steel-framed buildings. The Concrete Institute was formed in the same year that Guy Maunsell began working for Somerville; it became the Institution of Structural Engineers in 1922.

In the words of one engineering historian, 'the quite fantastic civil engineering achievements of the twentieth century are due to the availability of large quantities of good quality steel and concrete, and to the engineers' knowledge of how to use them to the best effect'. It was the combination of the two materials, in the form of reinforced and, later, prestressed concrete, that revolutionised civil engineering. Guy Maunsell became involved at just the right time.

Guy Maunsell's expertise with concrete was making him a valuable commodity. In 1909, this, combined with his skill in liaising with clients, won him his next job, with Easton Gibb & Sons Ltd, the main contractors for the Naval Dockyard at Rosyth in Scotland. Maunsell, a confident young man of 25, had a certainty about his own abilities that could appear arrogant and rude. He was interviewed by Alexander Gibb, later Sir Alexander, who went on to found his own very successful engineering consultancy. Gibb's great-grandfather had worked with Thomas Telford, his grandfather with Robert Stephenson. Later he would become a good friend of Guy Maunsell. But at the interview Gibb was not impressed. He told his young job applicant that he did not care much for his appearance. As Maunsell was on his way out of Gibb's office, he turned, looked Gibb straight in the eyes, and said, 'You know, you are making a big mistake. I could teach you a lot about concrete'. Gibb believed him. Maunsell joined the firm at Rosyth in June 1909 and finally departed in 1914, by which time he was the firm's chief sub-agent. But his prickly nature often made life unnecessarily difficult for him - during that time he actually left and rejoined the company three times.

The construction of the Naval Dockyard was an enormous undertaking. The 1,200 acre site stretched along the waterfront for 2½ miles. There were three docks, a power station, pumping station, workshops and stores. Land had to be reclaimed and an immense sea wall built. The project was expected to last seven years and six thousand men were employed, often working around the clock.

There was friction between client and contractor. The client, the Admiralty, believed its own plans for implementing the project could not be bettered. Alexander Gibb disagreed. In particular, he disputed the method of constructing the sea wall, which involved building 120 huge concrete monoliths as part of the foundations. The dispute lasted three years, with Guy Maunsell making any number of alternative proposals to overcome problems of the Admiralty's own making, until at last the client relented. For a man who was by nature impatient, especially with those who lacked his expertise, this was obviously a very trying time. But he was always thinking about how he could improve on designs for the benefit of the client, about what the most practical approach would be. Easton Gibb, because of the disputes between contractor and client, did not receive their final settlement until 1922, eight years after the work had been completed. Many years later, Maunsell wrote that

In the course of forty years' subsequent experience, I have never elsewhere encountered anything to compare with the desperate character of the engineering struggle which took place at Rosyth during these years, a struggle which Mr Gibb had to make against time and harsh natural conditions on the one hand, and against an unsympathetic lack of official understanding on the other.

The experience would serve Guy Maunsell well in future years.

Clients & Contractors – 1914-1939

In 1914 Guy Maunsell left Easton Gibb to join another contractor, R Thorburn & Sons, as chief agent. Thorburn was involved in the construction of two explosives factories for the government. The first, at Stevenston in the Scottish county of Ayrshire, was the reconstruction of the Misk Gelatine Works, which had been badly damaged after an explosion in February 1914. The second was the Pembrey Royal Ordnance Factory, built on the isolated sand dunes of southern Cefn Sidan in Wales. During the First World War, the Pembrey factory, producing Trinitrotoluene (TNT), was one of the largest of all munitions factories.

A watercolour of the French town of Bethune painted by Guy Maunsell on Christmas Eve 1918.

In 1917 Maunsell was called up as a commissioned officer in the Royal Engineers at the age of 33 and served in France for a year. He used his natural talent as an artist to capture a record of his war service through a series of watercolours. His sketchbooks were inherited by his daughter Maureen who said that they contained 'some very vivid sketches of the desolation of those terrible times'. In later years the firm he founded would use several of Guy's paintings to illustrate company Christmas cards. Among them were scenes of the village of Bethune and the ruins of Fleurbaix church, both drawn and painted

Three of the reinforced concrete ships built in 1919 at Shoreham for which Guy Maunsell was responsible.

in 1918. The inhabitants of Fleurbaix used the latter for the front page of their Municipal Bulletin in 1993.

Maunsell developed his existing skills in the management of men in the trenches but somewhere someone in authority realised that Maunsell's talents were being wasted at the front. During the First World War a shortage of steel coincided with a huge demand for more ships. This encouraged the authorities to investigate the construction of merchant vessels from concrete. It was not a new idea. It could be traced back to 1848 when a Frenchman, Joseph Louis Lambot, made a small concrete dinghy. In the 1890s an Italian engineer, Carlo Gabellini, was producing concrete barges and small ships commercially. But there was a limited supply of people with the knowledge and practical experience of working with concrete. So Guy Maunsell was called back home and sent as chief engineer to the Westminster offices of John Ver Mehr. Ver Mehr was building reinforced concrete ships, using a shipyard at Shoreham in Sussex. Maunsell was in charge of designing the shipyard and constructing the concrete tugs and other vessels, an experience on which he would draw for several of the schemes he prepared during another world war more than 20 years later.

He quickly demonstrated to the government his talent for combining innovation with practicality. In October 1918 he was asked by the Comptroller General of Merchant Shipbuilding to suggest ways of improving the construction of the concrete ships being built at Shoreham while reducing their cost. By using precast concrete frames and slabs, Maunsell achieved considerable savings in materials and manpower, both of which were very scarce in wartime Britain. Orders were placed for 15 concrete tugs, although only 12 were built before the war ended. The completed tugs all had names beginning with 'Crete', such as the *Cretemast* and the *Cretestream*. Half of them averaged 267 gross tons, the other half 660 gross tons.

During his time with Ver Mehr Guy Maunsell also assisted the Admiralty with a secret construction scheme that formed part of the Admiralty's anti-submarine strategy. By 1917, German U-boats had almost succeeded in cutting off vital supplies of food and raw materials to the UK, decimating merchant shipping and making it treacherous for ships to reach British ports. From late 1917 until the end of the war, six thousand Royal Engineers worked day and night to construct a series of huge reinforced concrete towers, 180 feet high by 160 feet wide, weighing 10,000 tons each, as part of the defences against enemy submarines. The £12 million plan (worth £411m in today's values), code-named *Project MN*, envisaged a dozen of these towers stretching across the English Channel from Dungeness in Kent to Cap Gris Nez in France, with other defensive devices, such as anti-submarine netting, lying in between. Cutting off the Channel as a route for the submarines to the North Atlantic would have reduced by a third their available operating time. When peace was declared in November 1918, only two towers had been finished. One of the finished towers was later used as the Nab Lighthouse in the Solent off the south coast of England; the other was broken up. But the method by which these towers were built – towing them out to sea from the safe waters of Shoreham harbour and flooding them so that they sank onto the seabed – influenced Maunsell's later work on the Storstrom Bridge in Denmark and on the Thames Estuary Special Defences during the Second World War.

By the time the war finished, Guy Maunsell had accumulated several years' experience of working not only with concrete but also with the Admiralty. It looked as if he would carve out a career for himself in government service. Confirmation of this appeared to come from his appointment in 1919 to work under Alexander Gibb, now chief engineer at the Ministry of Transport. In fact, his government career would be quite short – although transportation and marine engineering would become the core interests of his future.

Maunsell's time at the Ministry of Transport illustrated his ingenuity and intellectual curiosity. It showed once again how his fertile mind was capable of dreaming up remarkable new ideas that remained eminently practical. The problem he encountered was that those in authority often tended to cast aside his proposals because they seemed so outlandish, without recognising how easily they could be implemented.

In January 1919 one of his first reports assessed the viability of a Channel tunnel, plotting the course of a single rail tunnel stretching 35 miles under the sea, which he estimated would cost £38

The Nab lighthouse, in the Solent off the south coast of England, began life during the First World War as part of the nation's anti-submarine defences.

million (worth a billion pounds in today's terms). At the end of the same year he reported on the use of sonic appliances. He had visited the Sonic Works at West Drayton in Middlesex, which the Admiralty had placed at the disposal of a Mr Constantinesco, the inventor of sonic appliances, during the war. Broadly speaking, these appliances used water or oil as a spring to transmit energy. In particular he reported on the application of sonic principles to abrading machines and chipping machines for carving out rock or chalk during the construction of tunnels. Experience had demonstrated that this application resulted in much greater efficiency than from the use of conventional compressed air drills. Maunsell, who also touched in his report on the use of sonic pistons for activating a machine gun firing through a propeller, forecast a brilliant future for sonic devices.

He was also asked to investigate the potential of rail, trams and buses for reducing the impact of suburban commuters upon congestion in central London. Tramways, he concluded, were the most cost-effective method but the need to create tramlines in existing roads would cause undue hindrance to existing road users. For that reason, he believed that rail would be the most efficient way of dealing with the problem, advocating the use of fast, non-stop trains travelling above and below ground.

Maunsell also assessed the feasibility of constructing a mid-Atlantic airbase to facilitate flights across the ocean. His report showed that he was well aware of the growing importance of air travel. Discussing the proposed transatlantic route, he remarked that

> *The proposed route from Europe would take off from Spain or Portugal, make two landings in the Azores group of Islands, another landing at Point Z, then a landing in Newfoundland and so on to New York. The weak point in this is that the route does not traverse the British Isles. From the British point of view the great southern detour via Spain and the Azores detracts very much from the attractiveness of the scheme because it cuts the British Isles out of the line of crossing and deprives this country of the advantages which may be expected to accrue to the possessors of the European air terminus.*

Since airplanes in the early 1920s were limited to a range of no more than 800 miles, Maunsell advocated either the development of airplanes with a much longer range or what he called 'a floating sea drome', consisting of a platform built on top of a concrete pillar secured to the seabed. The semi-submersible construction method he envisaged would later become the universally accepted way of anchoring platforms in deep water. He also prepared a scheme for a tidal barrage at English Stones on the River Severn.

None of these ideas was implemented. Guy Maunsell was frustrated. He did not want to spend the rest of his life making investigations and writing reports. He wanted to use his engineering talents creatively, to see his ideas translated into reality, into projects that would serve a useful purpose, not into words gathering dust on some distant shelf.

In the event, he lasted only two years at the Ministry. His post may have fallen victim to the savage government spending cuts implemented during the economic recession of the early 1920s; or he may have talked himself out of a job, a round peg in a square hole.

Whatever the reason, in 1921 Guy found himself out of work just as he was embarking on married life. He had met Geraldine Mockler, a secretary at the House of Commons, while he was working at the Ministry, and they married in April 1922. For more than a year, the impecunious couple existed on an annual allowance of £100 (£3,400 in today's values) from Geraldine's father, himself an Indian Army officer on a limited pension. With so little money, they moved to the Continent where the cost of living was much cheaper. They spent several months in the Dordogne region of France, living in boarding houses. Later they spent some time in Portugal. Geraldine was also an amateur artist and, while Guy occupied his time by sketching and painting water colours, she produced a series of woodcuts from cherry and boxwood. Most of these were later destroyed, burnt as firewood during the difficult years of the Second World War.

Eventually the couple returned to the UK. From what little evidence exists of Guy's life during the 1920s, he seems to have led the life of an itinerant engineer, wandering from project to project, working for contractors wherever employment could be found. He worked on a handful of overseas projects, notably a scheme for using dredgers on a river in Colombia and the No 3 Dock for the dockyard in Malta. At home he was involved in designing the shaft for an English salt-mine and several projects in Scotland, including the Falls of Clyde hydro-electric scheme in Lanarkshire, a power station in Galloway and the steelwork for the Kincardine Bridge. At Kincardine he renewed his friendship with Alexander, now Sir Alexander, Gibb who had formed his own consulting engineering practice, Sir Alexander Gibb & Partners.

Guy and his wife initially settled in Rosyth while Guy was working mainly in Scotland. Their daughters Maureen and Rosalie were born in 1927 and 1930. Shortly after Rosalie was born, the family moved to Lanark to take up residence in Clyde Cottage, which Guy had designed himself.

Work was in short supply. The depression of the early 1930s brought mass unemployment and cuts in public expenditure even more savage than those of ten years earlier. But Guy was fortunate enough to keep working, moving from firm to firm and contract to contract. In 1931, when the depression was at its worst, he joined the respected engineering company, Dorman Long, as agent for the widening of Putney Bridge over the Thames in London. The company was then invited to become part of a consortium invited to construct a new bridge, the Storstrom Bridge, linking the islands of Lolland and Falster to Zealand in Denmark. The Bridge was intended to improve the flow of traffic to and from Copenhagen. Guy was appointed managing director of the company formed by the consortium, the Anglo-Danish Construction Company. Guy moved his family with him to a flat in Copenhagen. His daughter Maureen later remembered that the winter was so cold that the harbour froze while 'spring was endless – a glaring white sky, flat, windswept fields and a bleak east wind'. In the summer the two girls collected dandelions for making wine and paid several visits to the celebrated statue of the Little Mermaid on the harbourside.

The construction of the Storstrom Bridge was one of the highlights of Guy Maunsell's career as an engineering contractor and cemented the sympathy and understanding he always had for contractors in overcoming the practical difficulties of implementing

The Storstrom Bridge, linking the islands of Lolland and Falster to Zealand in Denmark, was completed in 1937. Guy Maunsell was closely involved in the early part of its construction, development techniques he employed on major projects many years later. Sixty years later, when Maunsell returned to Denmark to work on the Copenhagen Metro, senior managers visited the bridge to see at first hand the work of the founder.

engineering designs. The Bridge was a major steel structure, stretching more than 3,200 metres between abutments. It included 47 plate girder spans, each 58 metres long, with three bowstring girder bridges forming the main 138 metre long navigation opening. Guy applied his instinctive engineering brain to the problem of constructing the bridge. He bought two sea-going barges, and linked them with a deep lattice girder itself part of a twin tower crane capable of lifting a complete viaduct span in one piece. This was a great success and nearly three decades later Guy drew on this experience for his initial plans for the erection of the Gladesville Bridge in Australia.

The Storstrom Bridge, the longest in Europe at the time, was not completed until 1937. By then, Guy was no longer in Denmark. Ralph Freeman, later Sir Ralph, whose father founded the consulting engineering practice of Freeman Fox & Partners, was also working for Dorman Long at the time and had worked under Guy Maunsell during the widening of Putney Bridge over the Thames in London. He was sent out to Denmark in 1936, where he heard it rumoured that Maunsell had been forced to leave because of the jealousy of the then manager of the bridge department. Freeman recorded that the bridge was nevertheless completed according to the procedures Maunsell had already laid down.

Whether or not there was any truth in the rumour, Maunsell was in any case contemplating returning to the UK in early 1935. By then, he had already been offered a directorship with

Wilson Lovatt & Sons Ltd, a house-builder and general contractor. The British economy was picking up, fuelled by cheap loans, so housebuilding was booming. In February 1935 Guy decided to take advice from Hugh Beaver whom he knew from working with Alexander Gibb. Beaver was a partner at the time in Gibb's firm. He later directed the Ministry of Works for the British government during the Second World War, for which he was knighted.

Beaver advised his friend to reject the offer. The work, he believed, would not be challenging enough for him. Why didn't he come and join Sir Alexander Gibb & Partners? Beaver was sure they had plenty of intriguing problems more suited to Guy's talents. Guy consulted his wife. Beaver heard nothing more. In May 1935 he wrote again to Guy, asking if he had decided what he was going to do when he left Denmark in July. This time he was more specific about the projects that might interest Maunsell, one concerning the outer bar of Rangoon harbour, the other, a new bridge at Rosyth. He even outlined a possible working arrangement between Maunsell and Sir Alexander Gibb & Partners. Guy would act for Gibb on a consultancy basis. The firm would give him an office and expect him to give priority to their work but he would also have the freedom to offer his services elsewhere.

Guy accepted Beaver's offer. It was the start of his second engineering career, this time as a consulting engineer. The family returned from Copenhagen to take up temporary residence with Guy's father-in-law in Newton Abbot in Devon. Eventually Guy found a property, Hilden House, near Tonbridge in Kent, within commuting distance of Gibb's London offices. At Hilden there was space for a large vegetable garden which became Guy's principal recreation, a complete antidote to the pressures of engineering design.

He immersed himself in his work. His fertile mind was always dreaming up new ideas. Maureen Maunsell later wrote that 'whenever an idea for a design came to mind – a bridge, a harbour, a tunnel or anything, my father took out his extremely sharp pencil and drew it out. The newspaper, a letter, an envelope or the current library book would be covered in scribbles and designs made during a train or bus journey or just wherever he happened to be'.

In January 1937 Maunsell renewed his agreement with Gibb for three years and moved

A watercolour sketch of the Rangoon river done by Guy Maunsell in 1930.

into the latter's offices at 31, Queen Anne's Gate, in London. From Gibb he was given two staff, his secretary, Mrs Patterson, and a draughtsman, David Weller. Both of them stayed with him. Mrs Patterson retired through ill-health in October 1955. Although she was 14 years younger than Maunsell, she looked after him like a mother hen, guarding him from unwanted visitors. Weller, who also became Maunsell's photographer, died in 1972 while still working for the firm Guy Maunsell founded in 1955.

One of the major projects that taxed Maunsell in the late 1930s was the detailed design for the reconstruction of Thomas Telford's famous suspension bridge over the Menai Straits at Anglesey in Wales. It is acknowledged as one of the greatest of iron bridges and a testament to Telford's genius as both builder and organizer. Maunsell was no doubt an admirer of Telford and would have appreciated the meticulous care with which the bridge had been built. When it was finished in 1824, it had incorporated 16 iron chains, each weighing 25 tons, embedded into solid rock at each end of the suspension bridge. By the late 1930s, their replacement with steel chains was overdue. Work began in 1938 and, without any disruption of traffic, was completed in 1940. By then, the Second World War had begun so, in order to deny the enemy any information that might be of technical benefit, details of the Menai Bridge scheme were kept secret.

Maunsell never wanted to become a specialist. He enjoyed the challenge of tackling a wide variety of different engineering problems. Among his more mundane projects, he prepared bills of quantities for a fuel reservoir at the Rosyth oil fuel depot, drew up an estimate for a Rumanian naval base and completed a design for a marina and yacht basin at Southend-on-Sea in Essex.

His talent for innovation was displayed in a new method of tunnel construction he devised in 1938. This was essentially a variant on the immersed tube system which had been developed in the USA in 1903. Being an intensely practical engineer, born of years working on site, Maunsell devised his tunnelling technique, which he named *Tubelayer*, with two main aims – the cheaper construction of stronger tunnels. It was a method which applied only to tunnels built at relatively shallow depths, penetrating soft ground beneath river beds or the foreshore; it did not apply to deep tunnels or tunnels driven through rock. In his paper, he suggested it might be used for the proposed tunnels under the Thames at Blackwall and Woolwich. He also believed it might provide an alternative to the bridges being proposed across the Humber, the major waterway serving the port of Hull on the English east coast, and across the Severn in the south-west of England, both of which had been repeatedly deferred because of objections from navigation interests.

Maunsell also declared that the *Tubelayer* system would be a much safer method of construction. He was a practical man, so his ideas, although novel, were never produced for their own sake, and he never courted danger unnecessarily. This was an evident characteristic of the maritime schemes he would design for the Admiralty during the Second World War.

Maunsell & The Second World War –
1939-1945

Ideas overflowed from Maunsell throughout the war. He worked harder than ever. His daughter Maureen recalled that her father 'lived for his work'. Wartime conditions also compelled him to spend more time in the family's huge vegetable garden as the gardener, garden boy and maid all left to take up war work. The house was divided and part let. Sheep kept the grass down and Maunsell bought his first cow. He became very fond of cows and eventually moved to a small dairy farm, Jersey Farm, two miles from Hildenborough in Kent.

Maunsell the engineer was in his element. His talent was recognized by the authorities, although this was given grudgingly by the engineers he came into contact with, who often saw only bizarre ideas outside their comprehension. Serving officers, who could see the practicality of his schemes, were much more enthusiastic about them. And he had two staunch supporters in positions of influence, Alexander Gibb and Hugh Beaver. He submitted a plethora of schemes for defence against the enemy. These fell into two groups – those which were adopted by the authorities and those which were never used.

Inevitably more of Maunsell's schemes fell into the latter category than the former yet they could never be dismissed as impractical. That ran entirely counter to the way Guy Maunsell thought. They were all practical, simple and cost effective. In wartime, when building materials and skilled labour were in short supply, the authorities were forced to look more seriously at Maunsell's ideas. Nor could they overlook his allied skills in man management and an appreciation of the needs of the contractor.

The proposal he made for a submersible observation post, made in November 1939, might seem strange today. It seemed even stranger then that enemy vessels and aircraft might be detected through the use of radio waves. Radar was still being developed and was top secret. So Maunsell's suggestion of a manned buoy made from reinforced concrete, equipped with a crow's nest, towed out to sea and submerged at will by a five-strong crew, was not at all ludicrous. He described the purpose of his idea as the provision of

> *a type of fixed observation vessel which can be stationed at any selected point in the ocean and from whence a continuous watch can be kept upon the movements of all craft whether on, above or below the surface. It is intended to be supplementary to the ordinary patrol service carried out by ships and aircraft and to provide a chain of observation vessels at comparatively small cost and risk in all weathers.*
>
> *The individual vessel is designed so as to be as nearly as possible immune from damage by enemy attack. It can be towed out to its position and established without any previous preparation in the space of a few hours. The crew required to operate the vessel consists of five men who would no doubt have to be relieved by a fresh crew after a spell of one or two weeks on duty.*
>
> *It is intended that each observation vessel shall be provided with submarine listening apparatus and also with wireless so that it can communicate with either a central receiving post or with the nearest naval patrol on duty in the locality.*
>
> *A more elaborate type of vessel could be designed on the same principle so as to mount a searchlight and a gun or guns but the observation vessel herein described has on purpose been limited to its smallest and most economical proportions and is without armament.*

The scheme was never implemented but remained a classified secret in the UK until 1994.

Maunsell responded to any challenge thrown his way. As the Germans pressed on into France and the Low Countries, one of their main aims was to capture and destroy as many airfields as possible to consolidate their own superiority in the air. What was required, Maunsell was told, was a simple and speedy way of constructing emergency airfields without the need for skilled labour or scarce materials. Just one month after submitting his scheme for the submersible observation post, he came up with a solution. He envisaged the centralised daily production at a coastal factory of up to 8,000 concrete sleepers, creating a substantial advance stock of pre-cast sleepers which could be shipped out by trucks on demand to the site of the proposed airfield. The sleepers would be laid roughly on previously levelled ground, one beyond another, embedded by the trucks travelling along them as they were laid. Maunsell's scheme was twice as fast, dispensing with the production of concrete on site, the use of shuttering and the need for light railways to transport the concrete. The pre-cast sleepers were easily handled and transported, especially from one central point of distribution, and produced a saving in materials of about one-third over the alternative. Maunsell emphasised how 'speed of construction, ease of transport and centralisation of manufacture are the fundamental factors ruling in this case and it is these functions which the proposals are designed to perform'. He was, he added,

> *an engineer who has been engaged for over thirty years in carrying out very large construction works for firms of British contractors and ... the conclusions stated in this memorandum are therefore the result of a very long and very practical experience in field works.*

The scheme was overtaken by events as the Germans rapidly forced the British Expeditionary Force back to Dunkirk and it too was never put into practice.

Another idea despatched to gather dust in some official filing cabinet was sent in by Maunsell only two weeks after his proposal for the construction of emergency airfields. He adapted an idea he had known about from the First World War when a timber importing firm had used a timber raft to carry timber along the coast. Using his experience of the large timber-built temporary works for the Storstrom Bridge, Maunsell developed a design for a large sea-going timber lighter capable of being towed by tugs. Each lighter would carry up to 3,500 tons of timber. Both timber and shipping were scarce resources during wartime and Maunsell believed that building lighters from timber at the point of departure would free up shipping for other uses while still enabling the import of a significant volume of timber. The authorities, on the other hand, saw little point in the idea since they were already implementing plans to use home-grown timber to supply all the nation's needs.

From Maunsell too came the development of the idea which would lead to the Mulberry Harbours, the reinforced concrete artificial harbours so vital to the D Day landings in Normandy in June 1944.

The original idea was not Maunsell's; it came from an army officer, Lieutenant-Colonel Wilson, based in the War Office, in the aftermath of Dunkirk. Nor was Wilson the first to put forward such a suggestion. The principles employed in the Mulberry Harbours were the same as those used to construct the breakwater at the French port of Cherbourg in the eighteenth century – floating prefabricated units into position and sinking them on to the sea bed. In 1917 Winston Churchill had drawn up plans for capturing enemy territory using flat-bottomed barges or caissons to form an artificial harbour. Wilson asked Maunsell if he could put some flesh on the bare bones of the idea. In December 1940 Maunsell wrote to the War Office that Wilson had suggested to him that

structures similar to some which the writer has designed for the Admiralty ... might
be built and afterwards used to form berths for ships supplying troops landing or operating
upon enemy territory.

Maunsell's plan envisaged ready-made concrete structures towed across the Channel and speedily erected on the coastal foreshore, forming jetties or harbours to accommodate vessels of up to 5,000 tons for the discharge of cargo. Once again Maunsell took into account wartime difficulties. He emphasised simplicity and practicality. The structures would be built with unskilled labour, using readily available materials, in one standard unit at a low cost. They would be seaworthy and of an optimum size which would prevent them being displaced by wave action and breaking up on uneven ground. Maunsell wrote that 'the advantage of the system is mainly in the speed of assembly and in the quality of the berthing accommodation provided. A fleet of tugs and units approaching a coast at dawn could construct a five unit jetty ready for two or three ships to tie up alongside and unload within, say, five hours of the first landing. In calm weather conditions, the berthing accommodation would compare with that provided in a regular port and might be made serviceable, according to local conditions, in all moderate weather'. He estimated that each unit would cost £30,000, equivalent to more than £1 million today. His idea was filed away. Perhaps the timing was not right. Britain at the end of 1940 was more intent on survival than contemplating the invasion of enemy territory.

A similar idea occurred to a Welsh engineer, Hugh Iorys Hughes, a year later. The authorities failed, as they had with Maunsell's plan, to recognise any potential in the idea. But Hughes's

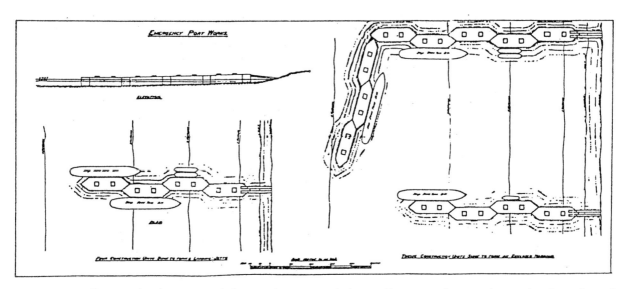

Guy Maunsell is credited as one of those who inspired the Mulberry Harbours, the artificial reinforced concrete floating harbours so vital to the D-Day Landings in June 1944. This is his sketch proposal made in December 1940.

brother was a naval officer and he drew it to the attention of more senior officers. Even so, when the government formed a committee of engineers and contractors (without inviting Maunsell) specifically to look into the design of an artificial harbour in September 1943, their scheme mirrored Maunsell's work.

There has always been some dispute in deciding who should be credited with the invention of the Mulberry Harbours. Historians mention Hughes alongside Professor J D Bernal, a prominent physicist, and Vice-Admiral Hughes-Hallett, Naval Chief of Combined Operations. Maunsell is usually over-looked. But, according to the biographer of Earl Mountbatten, the British military commander, Hughes-Hallett himself told Mountbatten that the inspiration for the Harbours came from Maunsell who had shown him his plans in 1940. It was only thanks to the promotion of Hughes-Hallett to such a senior position that the idea for the Harbours was given any serious consideration. He obviously had an instinctive sympathy for innovative and practical engineering. The scheme was derided as impractical by officials and officers, British and American, and Hughes-Hallett had to work hard to gain acceptance for the idea. It proved brilliantly successful. Maunsell was always grateful for Hughes-Hallett's sympathetic ear and, after Hughes-Hallett had retired from the Navy, lent him an office at his Victoria Street premises in London.

Maunsell, who, according to one of his staff, was always happiest when he was playing with water, also designed a motorised and submersible reinforced concrete and steel gun tower specifically for the D Day landings. It was intended to support an invasion of enemy territory by establishing heavy gun batteries close to the beach line overnight. A heavily armoured turret formed the bridge deck of a catamaran, raised on steel legs above supporting concrete hulls. It could be scuttled in shallow water but refloated for further use. The request to develop the idea came directly from the British prime minister, Winston Churchill. A prototype was actually built in 1943, trials were held in the Thames estuary and the Admiralty accepted the vessel into service as the Landing Craft Gun (Tower). But it was superseded by more mobile rocket-firing fighter aircraft which provided closer support for ground forces so no more were built. The original was sold off after the war to end its days in Hong Kong where it was used to recover sunken yachts.

The idea for a 'flush deck freighter', made from reinforced concrete, sailing across the Atlantic with its decks awash to avoid detection by enemy submarines, came from Maunsell's experiences during the First World War. The idea was considered by the authorities in 1943 but eventually discarded.

Maunsell's main contribution towards the war effort is usually regarded as the naval sea forts that originally attracted Colonel Wilson's attention. Maunsell's achievement has been little recognised until recently when the enthusiastic advocacy of his cause by local Kent historian Frank Turner has gone some way to redressing the balance.

Maunsell's Naval & Army Sea Forts, constructed during 1942 and 1943, played a key role in protecting Britain's shipping and major ports during the Second World War. In terms of their design and construction, they are still regarded as some of his most innovative works. Today surviving examples of his Army Sea Forts are being preserved because of their historical importance. This is the Knock John Naval Sea Fort plunging to the seabed in August 1942, watched from HMS Campbell (in the background) by Lord Louis Mountbatten, Admiral Sir Bruce Fraser, General Pile and others.

Maunsell's Naval Sea Forts began life in October 1940 as 'A Proposal To Establish Martello Towers For The Defence Of The Thames Estuary'. Martello Towers were the defensive coastal fortifications erected by the British in Britain and throughout the British Empire from the early nineteenth century onwards. Maunsell's paper was in response to a request for advice from the Harbour Master of the Port of London Authority, Commander E C Shankland.

In fact, Maunsell had first come up with idea several months before in a paper submitted in May 1940 to the Admiralty entitled 'Marine Fort No 3'. In this he had described something very similar to the scheme enshrined in his October proposal. This was a small, strongly protected fort, projecting above water but resting on the sea bottom, which could be built cheaply and quickly. Maunsell, at the time of Dunkirk, when invasion was a real threat, envisaged a string of such forts off the Dutch and Belgian coasts, acting as observation posts on the movement of enemy aircraft, warships and troop transports.

Maunsell went to great lengths in explaining how the fort was to be built, something that was a characteristic of his engineering career.

> *The form of construction is extremely simple and has been designed so as to lend itself to speedy erection. The pontoons can be built on light slipways on any river foreshore in tidal water and after they have been floated, the pedestal and citadel would be rapidly constructed on the pontoons by pouring concrete in prepared shuttering. The time taken to construct one of these Forts would be two months. A number of the Forts could be built simultaneously in the Port of London, so that within three months from the start, several Forts can be made available.*

This was the time when Britain was in most peril. The German airforce was blitzing British cities, the German navy was destroying British merchant shipping and doing its utmost to cut off badly needed overseas supplies. Commander Shankland was concerned about the magnetic mines being used by the Germans to sink shipping in the Thames estuary. The mines sank to the seabed and were almost undetectable until another ship was blown up. Shankland wanted a method of deterring the placing of mines or at least marking where they had been laid. He believed that constructing a series of forts across the estuary, stretching 26 miles from Margate in Kent to Clacton-on-Sea in Essex, would meet both these objectives. He turned to Maunsell for help with the engineering and construction details.

Maunsell believed that the scheme for three forts was entirely practicable and could be completed within six months at a cost of £81,000 (nearly £3 million today). Drawing on his previous proposal, he suggested a structure made of reinforced concrete, consisting of two parts, a pontoon foundation and a citadel superstructure. The fort, once completed, would be towed out and sunk into position. The pontoon, 55 metres long by 25 metres wide, was thick enough, Maunsell wrote, to 'sustain a great deal of damage without affecting the stability of the structure'. The superstructure, 18 metres long by 12 metres wide, standing eight metres above the pontoon, had reinforced concrete walls and a roof massive enough to withstand shellfire and small bombs. The profile of the structure was intended to make the fort difficult to hit with heavy bombs. Each fort would carry two six-inch guns, one anti-aircraft gun and two searchlights, with a crew of 55 officers and men.

Within a week of submitting his proposal to the Admiralty, Maunsell was asked to arrange a meeting to discuss it in more detail. It was at this meeting that Maunsell met Hughes-Hallett, then a naval captain, for the first time. Maunsell was accompanied by Sir Leopold Saville, a partner in Sir Alexander Gibb & Partners, and Hughes-Hallett by the Vice-Chief of Staff. As a result of this meeting, Maunsell was asked to prepare the design for a series of four twin-tower forts, each equipped with two 4½ inch guns. This he submitted in early November 1940.

Maunsell became impatient and frustrated. For weeks at a time he would hear nothing from the Admiralty. Then, having finally been asked to send design details at the end of December, he was invited to visit the Director of Naval Construction, Sir Stanley Goodall, in Bath. He was greatly disappointed at this meeting on 20 January 1941 to hear Sir Stanley pour a good deal of cold water on the proposal. Sir Stanley said he had been advised that the fort was inherently unstable and would probably capsize before it was sunk in position. In addition, he suggested that the forts, if they were built at all, should be built as a speculative venture. Maunsell's professional pride was wounded by the accusation that his designs were weak and he could not understand how the Admiralty could believe that any contractor would be willing to carry out the work speculatively in wartime. Maunsell returned to London, checked his calculations, satisfied himself they were correct and built a two metre long scale model which he offered to demonstrate to Sir Stanley. Maunsell's offer was rejected. Nothing more was heard and it seemed as if the Admiralty were determined to shelve the project.

One way or another, Maunsell managed to have a word in the right ear and at last on 6 March 1941 he met the Controller of the Navy, Vice-Admiral Fraser, who asked him to press ahead without further delay. Maunsell and Sir Alexander Gibb & Partners were appointed joint engineers for the project. By late March, in consultation with Hughes-Hallett and others, they appeared to have agreed on the design details and the location for each of the forts. The forts would now have two 3.7 inch heavy anti-aircraft guns, two 40mm Bofors guns and radar equipment.

Yet those who thought they knew better within the Admiralty still believed the forts were unstable. To reassure them, Maunsell had to bring in an independent naval architect to check his own calculations. In May 1941 he also had to prepare a detailed written statement explaining exactly how it was proposed to sink the forts. This described how inter alia

> The Tower is intended to be completely built and equipped with its armament, furniture and stores while it lies moored afloat at the deep water jetty at the selected building site near Gravesend. When the time comes to float it out and ground it, the moveable furniture and equipment would be secured against damage by lashings or other means ...
>
> Floating out would only be undertaken in settled weather and preferably when the wind is in the West or North West. In the case of the sites more remote from Gravesend, a start would have to be made on the flood tide. In other cases a start may be made on the ebb tide, timing to reach the destination just before the time of low water. Two river tugs would be employed hauling on tow ropes passed around the forward tower and a towing speed of four knots irrespective of the tidal current is anticipated ...

After further detailed descriptions of the steps necessary to ground the vessel, he concluded that

> The proposed method does not constitute a definitely controlled operation in the sense that the movement once started can be arrested or altered but it does constitute an automatic method whereby the tower must reach its appointed station upon the sea bottom within the space of about fifteen minutes without any possibility of mishap and by means of three simple and gentle movements.

The frequent meetings he would endure during the naval forts project, either at the Admiralty or in his own office at 31, Queen Anne's Gate in London, often drove him to distraction. For instance, Maunsell had given every member of the crew on each fort their own bunk for he knew that comfort was essential in confined surroundings. This upset Admiralty officials who refused to accept that ordinary seamen should sleep in anything other than hammocks. Maunsell, who had also included central heating and air conditioning for the accommodation, would not back down. The Admiralty had to give way. On several occasions Maunsell, to prevent his suppressed anger from overflowing, excused himself from the meeting and went home, leaving his visitors waiting.

In the meantime, Maunsell had discovered and leased a disused and derelict cement factory at Red Lion Wharf on the south bank of the Thames between Northfleet and Gravesend. Maunsell had also found a suitable contractor, Holloway Brothers, already working on a power station only eight miles from Red Lion Wharf. He recommended that the firm was awarded a contract and, once the site had been cleared and prepared for production, the Admiralty asked Holloway Brothers to start work on 5 June 1941.

Maunsell had tentatively suggested that the first of the forts would be in place at the beginning of December 1941. This timescale was frustrated by Admiralty officials and the operation was not carried out until 11 February 1942. The Navy took charge and almost caused a disaster. Maunsell sailed down river on the fort that was to be sunk seven miles off the port of Harwich on the Essex coast. An error made by the naval officer in charge resulted in the fort being flooded only from one side. The fort tipped over at an angle of 35 degrees before hitting the seabed and righting itself.

John Posford filmed the whole incident. He was the resident engineer at Red Lion Wharf, sent from Sir Alexander Gibb & Partners to take over from his predecessor who had been unable to work with Maunsell. Posford managed rather better and later became Maunsell's first business partner. Maunsell certainly had a reputation for being difficult but he was a loyal friend to those he liked. He was also extremely good at developing networks of influential contacts

When Posford's film was seen by the Admiralty, those who had expressed doubts about the forts in the first place voiced their concerns even more loudly. As a result, the Admiralty demanded that the contract should be altered. They refused to accept any responsibility for the forts until they had been positioned. Posford was put in charge of sinking the remaining forts, each one being positioned perfectly.

But the senior naval officers accompanying the forts could not resist interfering. Maunsell too travelled with each of the forts. On one occasion he noticed that one of the tow ropes attached to the fort from the tug had not been slackened off. The officers with him blithely ignored his increasingly agitated remonstrations. The situation was saved by the tug captain who knew Maunsell well. He suddenly disappeared and a moment later the offending rope suddenly snapped, much to the apparent amazement of the captain.

The success of the overall operation obviously impressed the military authorities. Liverpool, the most important port on the west coast of the country, lying on the River Mersey, had recently been heavily bombed by the Germans so it was decided to extend the project to the Mersey estuary in an attempt to mitigate the threat. Maunsell drew up a new design for a fort with a single gun tower capable of resting on the soft sand of the estuary. The new single tower fort could be built much more quickly and, since no time could be lost in view of the danger, the go-ahead was soon given. Once again Maunsell and Sir Alexander Gibb & Partners were appointed joint consulting engineers. In October 1941 the Cleveland Bridge & Engineering Co Ltd won the £336,000 (worth £10 million today) contract to build 21 of the new forts, which became known as the Maunsell Army Sea Forts. Maunsell provided the most thorough guidance to Cleveland Bridge for the construction of the forts, making recommendations for how the various components should be made and assembled, together with an estimated rate of production.

Although Maunsell was happy to offer guidance and advice to the contractor, his responsibility was to his client, the Admiralty. Cleveland Bridge was preparing a site at Bromborough Dock for producing the forts. Maunsell had previously inspected the site. He knew that the area proposed for building the cofferdam was solid rock – he had taken off his shoes and paddled in the shallow water to test the ground himself – and advised Cleveland Bridge that explosives would be needed. When he failed to

Maunsell's Army Sea Forts were erected in the Mersey and Thames estuaries during 1942-43. While the Naval Sea Forts were intended to deter enemy aircraft from dropping mines in Britain's major seaways, the Army Sea Forts were designed to impede the progress of bombers on their way to wreak destruction in the London Docks. This is the Red Sands Army Fort, photographed in 1995.

receive the firm's plan of works in a reasonable time, Maunsell, in Frank Turner's words, 'jumped up and down and cajoled the responsible people into action'. It had no effect. In December 1941 Maunsell wrote to the firm in no uncertain terms. Again, there was no response. This time Maunsell contacted the Admiralty, suggesting the firm's contract should be cancelled unless there was a major improvement in performance. Eventually, Maunsell recommended the replacement of the site agent at Bromborough with the site agent from Red Lion Wharf. The change produced the improvement Maunsell wanted. The first naval fort in the Mersey estuary was positioned in October 1942, the last in July 1943.

The concept of the forts was now being embraced with enthusiasm by the authorities. In March 1942, as the last of the naval forts was being built, Maunsell was told that the Chiefs of Staff Committee had decided to erect another 49 army forts in the Thames estuary. While Maunsell must have been delighted by this outcome, his pleasure was moderated when he was told that the contract should be put out to tender. Maunsell could have understood why this might be done in peacetime but failed to understand why it should happen during wartime. Holloway Brothers had built up an experienced workforce of some 400 men. A new contractor would have to start from scratch. The result would be more expensive. In June 1942 Holloway Brothers submitted a tender of £724,000 (£21 million today). It was accepted, proving Maunsell's point on costs, but the firm had to wait until September before a decision was made. The programme was eventually reduced to 21 towers which were completed between May 1943 and December 1943.

Maunsell wrote a valedictory note on the project to the Admiralty early in January 1944. He drew out the lessons which for him would heavily influence the rest of his career as a consulting engineer and permeate the ethos of the firm he founded in 1955. He firstly described the successful completion of the project.

> *Constrained by circumstances to disregard the more prudent counsels of antiquity (matutine ara vespertinus pete tectum) the final floating out operation sailed afternoon on December 13, whereafter it transpired that the last of the Towers was grounded on the Shivering Sand in bright moonlight and bitter cold shortly after midnight on December 14, the writer being present. Six days later the bridge connecting the Tower with the other Towers of its group was floated out and hoisted up into position, so completing the whole construction programme.*
>
> *As was the case with the original Naval Forts and also the A.A Forts built earlier in Liverpool Bay, these Thames Estuary A.A Forts have been erected under the direction of the Civil Engineer in Chief, Admiralty, with what we believe may fairly be described as the maximum economy in the minimum time and without any serious difficulty or mishap.*
>
> *All the work in question was founded on the original conception of building individual units complete with all their equipment before leaving port so that they might then like Minerva emerge fully armed from the head of Mars. The general success and relative economy of the undertaking was based on this simple principle.*

More importantly, he believed,

The twin hulls of the Normandy bombardment tower catamaran under construction at Red Lion Wharf in September 1943.

From the technical point of view, these undertakings constitute a new departure in engineering practice and have furnished a precedent which is already being imitated in another connection and under other auspices.

The smooth working of the constructional programme derives from the fact that when making the design so as to fulfil the military requirements of accommodation, access and equipment, and so as also to fulfil the technical requirements of strength and stability, a very close watch was from the very start kept upon the question of ways and means. That is to say, the structures were designed with an eye to the way in which they could be built and to the way in which they should be floated, towed and grounded. All this was in fact most carefully planned in advance and the operational procedure was developed under our closest personal supervision in every detail.

He concluded by thanking the contractors, the responsible naval officers, the river pilot and the tug boat captain.

Red Lion Wharf continued in use after the completion of the sea forts programme. In response to a request from the Prime Minister, Winston Churchill, Maunsell submitted proposals for a submersible reinforced concrete and steel gun tower for possible use in the Normandy landings. This vessel, with a catamaran hull, supporting a reinforced concrete and steel pillbox with two six-inch howitzers, was designed to move under its own power and submerge just off the enemy coast, leaving only the guns above water. It was partially built at the Surrey Commercial Dock and finished off at the Red Lion Wharf in November 1943. Trials were conducted from Gravesend and took place in the Thames Estuary during November 1943. The Admiralty accepted the vessel into service as the LCG (T) Landing Craft Gun (Tower). But no more were built and it sold after the war. The purchaser took the vessel to Hong Kong and for many years it was used to recover sunken yachts and boats from the harbour.

The second most successful idea of Guy Maunsell's to reach fruition was the reinforced concrete floating dry dock. In June 1943, John Posford was having a drink in the Tilbury Hotel with Admiral

Tovey, who commanded naval operations in the area. Tovey was complaining about the number of landing craft being damaged during training exercises and the difficulty in repairing them. The Admiralty had told Tovey that there was no chance of making any slipways available for the minor repairs required. He had also been told that steel was too scarce to make any floating dry docks.

Posford, who knew Maunsell had already submitted a proposal two months earlier for making floating dry docks from reinforced concrete, reported the conversation to Maunsell. Maunsell's initial idea had met without any response so he scaled down his proposal and resubmitted it. This time the idea reached the Civil Engineer-in-Chief, Admiralty, but, unsurprisingly, after some delay, Maunsell was summoned to Whitehall to be told for the second time that one of his ideas was quite unsound and such a structure was bound to capsize. Maunsell was furious. He rose from the table and, as he left, was especially blunt in his views –

Maunsell's reinforced concrete floating dry docks, built between 1943 and the end of the war, were so efficient that the techniques he used were later adopted by the US Navy. Several of the original floating docks are still in use around the world. This shows the first of them at the Red Lion Wharf site at Northfleet.

Gentlemen, as you know, I live on a dairy farm at Hildenborough in Kent. When I leave the office, I go home and the first thing I do is to go into the field where my cows are and discuss my day with them. I must say, I get more bloody sense from them than I ever get from talking to you!

Maunsell's outburst was understandable but it won him few friends in high places. Respect, as far as he was concerned, had to be earned and certainly did not come automatically with an increasing weight of gold braid on the cuffs of a uniform. He would listen to other points of view but never hesitated to tell people if he did not agree with them. This did not endear him to those who refused to recognise how much more talented Maunsell was as an engineer. This tended to leave him as something of an outsider within the profession and it is true that he often relished taking on the establishment. After the war he would write to the Institution of Civil Engineers that

> *my special methods for constructing Sea Forts and Floating Docks were bitterly opposed by certain established groups of Government engineers and naval architects. My ideas were nevertheless adopted and proved completely successful.*

Thanks to Posford, Maunsell contacted Tovey and told him the whole sorry tale. Tovey, incensed, overruled the Civil Engineer-in-Chief. Although the reinforced concrete dry docks cost just as much to build as steel dry docks, they used more widely available materials and could be completed more quickly. Maunsell completed his design and Holloway Brothers began making three 400 ton floating docks at Red Lion Wharf in August 1943. The first took three months to build; those which followed were completed at monthly intervals. This speed was attributable to the use of prefabrication, only the dock bottom and decks being cast in situ.

The first dock was floated on to the Thames in November 1943 and taken to Tilbury for trials where it was used to lift a crippled motor torpedo boat which had limped into the docks overnight. The trial, supervised by Posford, was a complete success. As a consequence, further orders followed for floating dry docks of varying lifting capacities. The largest was an 800 ton version, with better crew accommodation, capable of taking keeled ships. The smallest was one for 250 tons produced for the Inland Water Transport Department of the US Army. The docks were produced at the Bromborough yard as well as at Red Lion Wharf.

It was probably Maunsell's appreciation of Posford's efforts that led him to invite Posford to join him as a partner in 1944. In the new firm of G A Maunsell & Partner, Posford had a one-third share.

In the belief that the war in the Far East would continue for some time after the war in Europe ended in May 1945, it was decided to construct several yards overseas to produce Maunsell's floating dry docks. Two were built in India, at Vizagapatam and Cocanada, and another in Australia. In the event, through a combination of the usual delays from the Admiralty and the rapid defeat of Japan, all the remaining orders were cancelled.

Many of those already built gave sterling service around the world for decades. Some were towed as far as Ceylon (now Sri Lanka) and Singapore without mishap. A handful remain in use. They proved to be so efficient that the US Navy decided all its future floating dry docks should conform to Maunsell's design. And concrete floating docks are still being made around the world today.

The Admiralty had also accepted another plan from Maunsell geared towards military operations in the Far East. In June 1945 it was agreed – although only after the usual prolonged delays – to order two 'Accommodation Arks', built on similar lines as the reinforced concrete floating docks and designed as floating barracks with a capacity of 600 officers and men. With Maunsell and Sir Alexander Gibb & Partners as joint consultants, the arks were to be built in Northern Ireland and be ready to sail in mid-January 1946. Scarcely had the preparatory works been completed when the Japanese surrendered and the project was abandoned.

The Path to G Maunsell & Partners – 1945-1955

When the war ended, Guy Maunsell was in his early 60s. Unlike some of his peers and several lesser men, his undoubted contribution to the war effort went unrecognised by officialdom. He won some recognition from the Institution of Civil Engineers. Papers presented by Maunsell received the Coopers Hill War Memorial Prize and the Telford Prize, and he was invited in 1951 to deliver the prestigious annual James Forrest Lecture. But public honours never mattered to Maunsell. The achievement of practical and, wherever possible, elegant designs was always sufficient satisfaction for this brilliant if temperamental engineer.

After the war, Maunsell's relationship with Sir Alexander Gibb & Partners continued in exactly the same way as it had begun ten years earlier. Maunsell and his partner, Posford, were helped by as many as 70 staff seconded from Gibb to design a series of mainly industrial projects in the UK. Among them were oil refineries for Shell and factories for the Associated Ethyl Company and for Fisons.

As the work of the firm increased, a third partner was admitted to the firm. Richard Pavry had been the senior engineer on the Shell oil refinery contract. Between them, Guy Maunsell's two partners held more than half of the equity in the business, which became Maunsell, Posford & Pavry. Maunsell began to gather around him a group of young talented engineers with practical experience who were sympathetic to his views on the profession. Len Ramage came in 1949 after working as an engineer for several firms. He worked on a wide range of projects for Maunsell, including a dry dock in South Wales which, he said, 'gave me an introduction to the novel and most workmanlike designs produced by Guy Maunsell'. John Baxter met Guy Maunsell while he was working for Shell in 1948 and joined the firm in 1952. In 1950, when Maunsell visited the Middle East, he was introduced to a young man, Miles Birkett, who was working for a consortium of contractors. Two years later, in 1952, Birkett joined the firm and opened an office in Baghdad to supervise the construction of an oil refinery and a number of other projects, including three bridges. Then there was Peter Stott, a brilliant young design engineer. By the late 1940s Maunsell, Posford & Pavry employed 60 staff.

The oil refinery designed by Maunsell in Baghdad, another joint project with Sir Alexander Gibb & Partners, began an on-off relationship with Iraq for his firm that lasted throughout the rest of the century. This was another joint project with Sir Alexander Gibb & Partners.

Maunsell began to travel widely around the world, discovering for the first time that his talents and expertise commanded an international market. He went to the Far East, where the firm designed a scheme to stabilise the bank of the river Chao Phya which runs through Bangkok in Thailand; to Australia, where the firm was advising on a proposed terminal for flying boats, the dredging of the outer harbour at Fremantle and the proposed reconstruction of a bridge over the Hobart in Tasmania; and to the Gambia where a new jetty was being built at Mandinari. In Turkey he envisaged a bridge over the Bosporus and he devised several different proposals for the Istanbul authorities over the years, none of which was accepted.

In the spring of 1952 Maunsell visited Bangkok, stopping on the way in Colombo in Ceylon (now Sri Lanka) as well as Baghdad and Basra in Iraq. He wrote to one member of his staff that in Bangkok he had taken in three conferences, two power station inspections, one sugar refinery inspection, one Siamese play, one Chinese dinner, two construction job examinations, two Buddhist temple visits and several introductions to government ministers. In the days before air travel was commonplace, when the usual method of travelling long distances was to spend several weeks aboard a passenger liner, this was quite a schedule.

Even though Maunsell was approaching 70, he was still physically fit, thanks to work on his smallholding and cycling morning and evening to and from the local railway station when he was working in London. He was also adept at making himself comfortable on long journeys. His daughter Maureen recalled that her father 'was so vague and absorbed that discomfort did not really bother him. He could always go to sleep on a train or plane but unfortunately quite often failed to wake up in time, and when he overshot the station, it could be a weary business catching the next train back in the days when there was no petrol available for his wife to come in the car and when his bicycle was left behind at the wrong station'. John Read, a young engineer who joined the firm in 1951, remembered travelling by train with Maunsell from Edinburgh to London. Maunsell gave every appearance of being sound asleep but, when the ticket collector appeared, Maunsell, without opening an eye, retrieved his ticket, saying to Read, 'And you thought I was asleep'. Very few people caught out Guy Maunsell.

Despite his innovative ideas, he was in several respects an engineer of the old school. He hated propelling pencils, fountain pens and wristwatches. Before he arrived at the office every morning, the inkwells were filled, pencils sharpened and new nibs fitted to penholders. He had to be told when the time neared six o'clock, when he took a bus to Charing Cross station for his train home. His staff, who affectionately called him 'The Old Man', went in awe of him. Partly this was because of his enormous reputation and partly because of his fearsome temper. A slight man, he could be startlingly direct. He was also very inquisitive, always asking staff and colleagues for the reasons behind what they were doing, which could be unsettling for some junior staff. He could swear as well as anybody, especially on site, which probably accounted for some of the respect in which he was held by contractors. There was nothing aloof about Guy Maunsell. The smallest things could ignite his temper. There were usually warning signs. His colleagues came to recognise that when he came to the office wearing a bow tie, it was a sign of a storm on the horizon. Another was when pencil shavings started to fly across Maunsell's desk. Once John Read, helping him with calculations, said he would have to fetch his slide-rule. Maunsell, Read remembered, exploded – he calculated everything in his head. But Maunsell never held grudges. One young engineer, humiliated in public by Maunsell for something he had not done, received an equally public apology the following day. Sometimes Maunsell would apologise in a more oblique way. If he was upset, he would often vent his anger on whoever was nearest. The office accountant, Bob Wakefield, recalled that events the morning afterwards rarely varied. The injured party was invited into Maunsell's office, offered coffee and biscuits and a king-size cigar, and asked about his family – that was Maunsell's way of apologising.

His attitude to work and money was heavily influenced by the years he had been out of work, existing on little apart from fresh air. He was always a very hard worker, rarely taking time off. He did not believe in holidays. Family holidays were often combined with site inspections so that he should not waste any time. According to his daughter Maureen, he regarded paid annual holidays, which became usual after the Second World War, 'as being a totally unnecessary innovation'. He was frugal with money. Some years later, a first class train ticket was bought for him to travel to the official opening of a new dock he had designed. He returned it unused, asking for a refund, having bought himself a third class return. The office accountant, Bob Wakefield, who later recorded his reminiscences of Guy Maunsell, wrote that Maunsell 'made no comment but the message to me was nonetheless clear, that is, money is hard to come by, so don't throw it away'. His office was equipped with mainly second-hand furniture while his secretary, who first joined him in 1935, was given her first new typewriter in 1950.

The salaries and wages he paid his staff were below the going rate. Miles Birkett once summoned up the courage to ask Maunsell for a small increase in his salary. His employer sternly told him that his request was quite out of the question. Miles, embarrassed, left the office but discovered when he returned to his desk that a five pound note had been slipped into the book he had been carrying. It was not a huge sum but the gesture made an unforgettable impression on

Birkett. Maunsell was always concerned for his staff and would pay bonuses that, in a good year, more than made up the difference between what they were paid and what they should have been paid. He also sent each of them every Christmas a Stilton cheese, writing out their names and addresses on the parcels in his own hand. He enjoyed the annual staff outing, usually to a place of interest in Kent, followed by a visit to his home. Maunsell would join the coach at an agreed point, throwing his bicycle into a nearby ditch for collection later. The day concluded with dinner at a local hotel but occasionally Maunsell entertained staff to a buffet supper in the grounds of his home. Personally he could be very generous and several members of staff had reason to thank their employer for his spontaneous acts of kindness. When his younger daughter was married in 1956, every member of staff was invited to attend. He brought presents back for the women in the office from his travels abroad and often wrote personal letters to his colleagues, describing his progress overseas.

Guy Maunsell never stopped coming up with new ideas. In the early 1950s he designed another marine structure, a floating sea boring unit for the National Coal Board, for drilling at sea. Two were built. The first, completed on the north shore of the Firth of Forth in Scotland, was towed 14 miles to its first site and was subsequently repositioned seven times before being scrapped. The second, built at Blyth in north-east England in 1955, was used to determine the seaward extent of the local coalfield before being bought by Trinity House, the UK lighthouse authority. It replaced a lightship off the Lincolnshire coast.

Maunsell had never really been at ease with his partners. He preferred the company of the talented young engineers he had recruited to the firm after the war. Maunsell's partners, on the other hand, believed that it was time their ageing senior partner, now over 70, should retire. There was also a disagreement over the allocation of profits, with Maunsell insisting that staff should share in the firm's success. Matters came to a head during 1954 when Maunsell and Posford had a personal disagreement. This soured relations and precipitated the eventual clash. In October 1955 the partnership was dissolved. Posford and Pavry set up their own practice. Maunsell, with a handful of devoted but eager young staff, moved to a new office and established a new firm. For a man of his age, this was an act of enormous confidence.

Part 2
1955-1970

The Maunsell Vision

Beyond the age when most men would contemplate retirement, Guy Maunsell was starting all over again. With the four young engineers he took with him to temporary offices at 17, Queen Anne's Gate, courtesy of Sir Alexander Gibb & Partners, he established another new firm, G Maunsell & Partners. Determined to build a firm according to his ideals and beliefs, Maunsell's influence would spread across the globe through what became the Maunsell group of companies. The lessons he passed on would in turn be handed down to later generations of civil engineers who, even though they never met him, would venerate his name.

Maunsell set out his vision for G Maunsell & Partners with absolute clarity in a memorandum he prepared at the time the firm was established in 1955 (See Appendix I). The key principles which shine through this short document might be summarised as integrity, inclusion, fairness, practicality, transparency and unity. The importance of integrity was implicit in the declaration that the first duty of the partnership was to serve the interests of the client. The firm, Maunsell wrote, would always render a service in excess of the fees paid. Overcharging or under-performing he considered unthinkable. The principle of providing value for money has survived to this day.

Service to the clients, Maunsell believed, also included the development of a sympathetic and considerate relationship with contractors. This was almost unheard of among British consulting civil engineers, many of whom considered themselves a cut above the lowly contractor and made this plain in the way they dealt with them. But Guy Maunsell felt that the consulting engineer could serve the client more effectively by bearing in mind the practical requirements of construction. His early experiences conceiving practical methods on site had deeply affected him and he wanted to ensure that the firm never designed anything that was difficult to build. Maunsell was ahead of his time when he wrote that 'it will be our endeavour when we are designing works at the same time to plan the way in which those works are to be put into execution'. Practicality of design became one of the enduring characteristics of the firm. In Guy Maunsell's words, 'in all cases of difficult or heavy civil engineering work, we shall therefore attempt to plan the carrying out at the same time as we are designing it'. In this way the firm could save time and money for both client and contractor.

Maunsell believed that fairness and transparency applied to every member of staff as well as to clients and contractors. Each person, through his or her efforts, was entitled to share in the resulting benefits, financial or otherwise. This approach would help to create a more open relationship between partners and staff – Maunsell wanted to prevent 'the creation of too sharp a line of demarcation between partners and others'.

Finally, he believed it was very important that

> *the activities of the several partners, their associates, consultants and assistants shall be co-ordinated and remain under centralised control and shall not be allowed to disperse or separate out into watertight compartments.*

What he wanted was a unity of purpose, which could come about only if everyone within the organisation was aware of what was going on.

These principles – a concern for quality, for the client, for the contractor and for staff – formed the bedrock on which, over the next decade, Guy Maunsell's firm began to build an international business. Clients and contractors respected a firm that combined a down-to-earth approach to civil engineering with an undeviating professional integrity. The mutual support which Guy Maunsell encouraged among his staff, together with the relaxed working relationship at all levels within the firm, created, certainly in the early years, a common bond which unified those on opposite sides of the world. Unity was always a crucial aspiration among those responsible for running what became an international business; and their determination to uphold this principle was an important reason why the firm remained united.

These were not the only reasons for the growth of the firm during the 1950s and 1960s. Guy Maunsell's own reputation attracted creative and talented young engineers who became pioneers and innovators in their own right. Their example in turn brought a further generation of capable engineers to the firm and so the cycle repeated itself. Maunsell, John Baxter later recalled, 'was a very fine engineer, I fairly worshipped the ground he walked on. He had the courage as an engineer to do things which had not been done before ... if he decided he had the right sort of solution, the fact that it was new did not deter him in the slightest'.

There was never much arrogance in evidence in the firm, unlike several of their established rivals, a quality which clients appreciated. The partners in one part of the firm never believed that they were the fount of all knowledge; they were happy to share their accumulated wisdom and experience. They recognised talent and encouraged those with potential wherever it came from. So they were happy, as the firm expanded beyond the UK, to allow responsibility to be passed on to those overseas. At the same time, when the firm did not itself possess the skills required by clients, it never hesitated to bring in those who did have the required knowledge. From the very beginning, Maunsell employed external consultants wherever necessary.

Maunsell in the UK

Guy Maunsell was 71 when G Maunsell & Partners was founded. His four partners were all striking individuals.

John Baxter was the oldest, born in 1917. He had left school at 16 and achieved his civil engineering degree three years later. In 1957 he took over from Maunsell as the firm's managing partner. He went on to become President of the Institution of Civil Engineers in 1976 and also chaired the Association of Consulting Engineers in the UK. During the high inflation of the early 1970s he chaired the working group which derived and developed the Baxter Formula on fluctuations in construction prices in 1975. It is still in use today. Unlike Maunsell, Baxter, who was awarded the CBE (Commander of the Order of the British Empire), became part of the professional establishment.

Baxter was a fitting successor to Maunsell. A courteous, humane man, the epitome of a gentleman, Baxter had a great sense of humour and a big, hearty laugh. He cared for his staff, always insisting on shaking hands with every one of them on the first morning of the New Year in the period before New Year's Day became a public holiday in England. He was respected enough for all of them to turn up for work that day, no matter how little sleep they may have had. When Peter Johnson joined the firm, he instinctively called Baxter 'Sir' only to be gently admonished. Only knights of the realm, Baxter told him, were entitled to be called 'Sir'. He was quite happy to be addressed as 'Mr Baxter' and, eventually, simply as 'John'. It was, recalled Johnson, part of Baxter's belief that no one in the firm should ever be intimidated by anyone else, no matter how exalted their standing. He was a relaxed manager whose practice of allowing his engineers to use their initiative at an early stage inspired loyalty and respect.

The other partners were Len Ramage, aged 33, gentlemanly and considerate, Miles Birkett, aged 29, sharp and enthusiastic, and the youngest partner, Peter Stott, only 28. Ramage and Birkett

John Baxter

Len Ramage

Miles Birkett

Peter Stott

The four new partners in G Maunsell & Partners all followed Guy Maunsell from his previous firm – John Baxter, partner 1955-1980, managing partner 1957-80; Len Ramage, partner 1955-84; Miles Birkett, partner 1955-72; Peter Stott, partner 1955-1963. Baxter (1976) and Stott (1989) were both Presidents of The Institute of Civil Engineers.

would remain with the firm for the rest of their careers but Stott would later carve out a successful career in public service after leaving the firm in 1963. After ten years directing transportation for the Greater London Council, he became the first director-general of the National Water Council and then Emeritus Professor of Engineering at King's College, London. He shared with John Baxter the double distinction of being awarded the CBE (1978) and being elected President of the Institution of Civil Engineers (1989).

The remainder of the original staff, known as the first eleven, after a cricketing term for the members of the first team, consisted of David Weller, chief draughtsman, and Harry Howard, draughtsman; Sylvia Welton, tracer and artist; John Read and Dudley Sewell, engineers; and Mrs Patterson, Maunsell's secretary. This small band of staff, who remained with the firm for the rest of their careers, would soon be joined by others.

The mid-1950s seemed a propitious time for Guy Maunsell to make his break from his previous partners and set up his new firm. Internationally, the innovations of wartime, including advances in building technology, such as prefabrication and mechanisation, and in computing, were applied to the post-war infrastructure rebuilding programme. Maunsell was excited by the way techniques for the use of prestressed concrete were being perfected for bridge building.

Making possible the use of beams and slabs with much longer spans, this had been invented by the brilliant French engineer, Eugene Freyssinet, in 1904. But prestressed concrete was not widely adopted until high tensile steel became commonly available. Its rapid advance in use came only after the Second World War. Prestressing the concrete enabled the stresses within it to be altered so that both the steel and the concrete could be used to their maximum potential. This allowed beams to be designed more efficiently and so they could be used for even greater spans and loadings. A prestressed concrete beam typically required 70 per cent less steel and 40 per cent less concrete than a reinforced concrete beam of the same loadbearing capacity.

Just as Guy Maunsell had been in the vanguard of those making the most of reinforced concrete, so the Maunsell firms would be among the pioneers in the adoption of prestressed concrete for bridges. This willingness to adopt new techniques was one of the key reasons why Maunsell remained one of the leading firms in its field.

The firm was also fortunate to be founded when the world's developed economies were moving out of post-war austerity into a sustained period of economic expansion. In the UK, where the firm began, and in Australia, where it established its first successful overseas operation, governments were investing in major public infrastructure projects to support their booming economies and more prosperous populations. It was for this reason that the firm established its reputation in highways and transportation. The drawback was that Maunsell became so closely identified with public clients and with bridges and roads that it became harder to break into other civil engineering sectors.

The other disadvantage which perhaps held the firm back during the 1960s was a lack of commercial astuteness. Guy Maunsell himself often had scant regard for profitability. In an age when fees were charged according to a set professional scale, profitability could be easily overlooked. Maunsell preferred to concentrate on the quality of the work done by the firm and the calibre of the staff it employed. As a partnership, the firm was managed by professional engineers who, no matter how capable they were as civil engineers, had little experience of the other skills required to run an expanding business. While Guy Maunsell never shrank from going out to look for work, this was done on a personal basis. Neither he nor his immediate successors embraced with much enthusiasm the idea of publicly promoting the firm to potential clients. Even Miles Birkett, who pioneered the firm in Australia, adhered to the example set by Guy Maunsell – Birkett's success essentially came from his personal enthusiasm and his boundless energy and, while he rarely failed to pursue a commercial opportunity, he was less interested in profitability than winning the work.

In the UK, after nearly a decade of post-war austerity, the last state controls on industry had been abolished in 1954 and the property market was beginning to boom. The country was entering a period of prosperity summed up by the phrase, 'You've never had it so good', apocryphally attributed to Harold MacMillan, who became prime minister in 1957. But the firm's first three years brought little reward in the UK, perhaps because of Guy Maunsell's prickly reputation, perhaps because his sympathy for the contractor was viewed with some suspicion by some potential clients, perhaps because of the unproven track record of the firm. Another reason was Maunsell's belief that the highest standard of service should be given regardless of the fee. At times he personally had to subsidise the firm's expenses and pay the staff bonuses. Bob Wakefield, the firm's long-serving accountant, later related how he was often called to see the bank manager 'to convince him that we were worth supporting in difficult times. I became quite adept at spinning yarns about large contracts that were about to come our way'.

Perhaps Maunsell felt that he would never receive proper recognition in the UK. He had found it hard enough during wartime. But he also knew from personal experience in the years immediately after the war that the market beyond British shores was much more receptive to his ideas. So, without enough work in the UK, Maunsell and his colleagues began to look overseas for work.

The first overseas project came in 1955. Guy Maunsell's lack of pretension impressed a visiting party of bridge engineers from Western Australia. Sent over to search for a suitable consulting engineer to design a new bridge across the Swan River in Perth, they had been condescendingly rejected by every other firm of consulting engineers they had met. Apparently it was almost by accident that they came across the nameplate on the door of the Maunsell practice. They had nothing to lose. Guy Maunsell saw them at once, gave them a sympathetic hearing and was invited to design what became the Narrows Bridge.

The Narrows Bridge over the Swan River at Perth was the first overseas project carried out by G Maunsell & Partners. Completed in 1960, it was added to Western Australia's heritage list in 1999 for its innovative design.

Another project was already as good as won. In 1952 the director of the Tasmanian public works department had asked the UK Ministry of Transport to recommend a consulting engineer to report on the storm-damaged condition of the existing floating bridge over the Derwent at Hobart. The Ministry's bridge engineer, Cyril Chettoe, recommended Guy Maunsell. Maunsell's personal reputation and his excellent, long-lasting relationship with clients had paid dividends. The State government accepted his recommendation for a new high level bridge although lack of funds delayed the award of a contract until 1956. These two early commissions paved the way for the creation of the firm in Australia.

At the same time the firm's partners were searching for other opportunities around the globe, visiting Australia, Singapore, Cuba, Venezuela, Sierra Leone and Iraq. By and large this resulted only in isolated international work. For example, in the late 1950s the firm was involved with two power stations at Bandur Masha and Agha Jari in Iran and another at Basra in Iraq. Any further ventures in Iraq were prevented by the bloody revolution which overthrew the royal family in 1958. John Baxter and Peter Stott both witnessed the revolution; Baxter was held in custody for two or three days for his own safety. In the Gambia, the firm worked on the Oyster Creek Bridge in 1958.

The Hammersmith Flyover, completed in 1961, made revolutionary use of prestressed concrete. This curving elevated motorway, running from west London towards Heathrow airport, was the first post-tensioned pre-cast segmental concrete structure in the UK. (Photograph by courtesy of Noel Foster.)

Here the innovative 'Gambia piles' were used for the foundations for the first time to overcome difficult ground conditions. Reinforced concrete was cast inside a steel casing and driven into the foundations by a hammer acting inside the casing. Again the willingness to adopt new techniques in the face of sceptics had proved to be justified. Four years later came the Brumen Bridge in the same country.

Guy Maunsell believed that it was only a matter of time before the firm, with its concrete expertise, would eventually start winning work in the UK. He noted how rising prosperity was creating an unprecedented rise in the number of private cars on the roads. In 1952 the figure stood at 2½ million, scarcely more than in 1939; by 1959 it had risen to 5 million. The spread of the motorcar became unstoppable as numbers exceeded 9 million in 1965 and 11 million in 1970. To accommodate this increase, the country embarked with relish on a steadily expanding programme of road building. The first short stretch of the M1, one of the first motorways in the UK, was opened in 1959, while the recommendations of the Buchanan Report in 1963 unleashed a host of urban motorway projects intended to improve the urban environment and relieve traffic congestion.

In 1955 one of Guy Maunsell's first decisions after founding the firm was to secure the services as a consultant of Cyril Chettoe. He came to Maunsell after retiring as chief engineer with the Ministry of Transport and remained with the firm until his sudden death in 1963. Maunsell clearly believed that the future of the firm in the UK would be based on an expansion of the road network. The breakthrough came in 1958, after Guy Maunsell had already handed over as managing partner to John Baxter. The firm was awarded the contract to design the Hammersmith Flyover, a curving elevated motorway stretching towards London's Heathrow airport. The client was the London County Council (LCC), one of the many public bodies on which consulting engineers were reliant at home and abroad. The disadvantage of this reliance was the way in which work fluctuated according to the fortunes of the national economy.

The design for the Hammersmith Flyover displayed the expertise of Guy Maunsell and his colleagues in the use of prestressed concrete, a material then little used in the UK. Hammersmith Flyover, completed in 1961, became the first post-tensioned pre-cast segmental concrete structure in the country. It was a revolutionary concept. Previously precasting had been used only for concrete beams, but here elements were erected and prestressed together to form a central box girder, complete with cantilever arms at intervals. These arms supported the side slabs, which completed the full width of the bridge deck. Among other innovative aspects of the structure, the prestressing used external strands located within the box and the columns were fixed to the deck with bearings at their base.

The design work for this pioneering structure was costly. Yet the cost of construction, reflecting Guy Maunsell's sympathy for the contractor and his constant awareness of what would work in practice, was much lower than using traditional reinforced concrete or steel. The trouble was that, as a result, the firm made much less money on the contract since its fees were calculated as a percentage of the construction costs. The LCC later made an ex gratia payment to cover the fee loss but the partners regarded it as worthwhile for placing the firm, in the words of one observer, 'in the vanguard of modern concrete design in the United Kingdom'. Another innovative aspect of the Hammersmith project was the use by the firm of elementary computers for calculations.

Guy Maunsell did not live to see the completion of the Flyover, dying on 20 June 1961 at the age of 76. He had finally retired from the firm two years previously through ill-health after suffering a heart attack. As a result, he and his wife had moved from Hildenborough to a house closer to Tunbridge Wells. Maunsell had always been interested in comparative religions and the occult and devoted much of his retirement to writing a book on the lives of the saints. He had just completed the book, written in his rather otiose style, in longhand with pen and ink, when he died.

Although during his lifetime he had never won the recognition that he deserved from his peers in the profession, the tributes that poured into the London office were generous. Lord Holford, the renowned international architect, who knew him well, called him a genius. Sir Hugh Beaver, who had encouraged him to become a consulting engineer, wrote that

He had a remarkable and inventive brain and it was only his own modesty that prevented him being known outside the engineering world as well as he should have been. It is not possible to deny that he did not suffer fools easily ... but I must say that I look back on the years I was working with Guy Maunsell as some of the most pleasant and most productive in my life.

Over the next few years the benefits from the Hammersmith Flyover came in a stream of contracts for the design of motorways and other new roads. No sooner was the Flyover finished than the firm was invited to design a section of the M4 motorway in South Wales; the Mancunian Way, an elevated urban motorway through Manchester; and Westway, running from White City to Paddington in London. The story of how the firm won the M4 motorway contract illustrates how quickly it had established its reputation. John Baxter was called to the Ministry of Transport to finalise the agreement on Westway; he was not allowed to leave until the Ministry had persuaded him to agree to carry out the motorway contract as well.

Following on from the success of the Hammersmith Flyover, Maunsell designed two further similar schemes, the Westway (seen here), running from Paddington to White City in London, and the Mancunian Way, an elevated motorway in the heart of Manchester. Both were completed in 1968 and incorporated innovative design techniques.

The Mancunian Way and Westway both incorporated the ideas of precast segmental construction. One advance over the Hammersmith design was the use of box sections with integral cantilever slabs. In those days the units were connected using a four-inch wide in situ concrete joint. Section Five of the Westway had precast units that were eight lanes wide, the biggest units built at that time. Westway also featured the innovative top-hat pretensioned box beam that had been developed by Maunsell as a way of creating a voided slab.

Westway, with its vast scale and innovative designs, convinced the partners to acquire the firm's first computer, affectionately known as Emily, in 1965. The investment involved was more than £100,000, a huge sum for the time and an indication of the firm's commitment to the use of modern technology. A brochure from the period stated that 'a computing organisation is operated in London where a digital computer, graphical plotter and automatic co-ordinate reader are installed. The equipment is used for computation, design and automatic drawing in various fields'. In 1968, a separate company was established in order to market the use of the computer in an era when few businesses possessed their own but the partnership refused to allow it to indulge in the distasteful commercial practice of marketing and it made little progress. The computer team in the London office, which grew to 15 people by 1970, led by Bill Griffith-Jones, developed a talent for making the most of the limited capacity of this early machine as well as writing dedicated programs. Part of this development included the purchase of an early flat-bed plotter in 1966, quickly and accurately creating line work that had previously taken hours to do manually. In 1968 Maunsell developed, for the UK Ministry of Transport, the first program to create perspective drawings for highway visualisation. The software was written by Roger Wright who managed the UK firm's IT facilities from 1970 until his retirement in 2002.

Westway's bold, uncompromising concrete design was in tune with the modern technological approach of Britain's new Labour government. Westway was completed in 1968, the same year as the Mancunian Way, once called Manchester's 'Highway in the Sky', intended to be the first part of an urban motorway network which was never completed. The inspiration behind the firm's pioneering span-by-span construction method of prestressed concrete hollow box beams with cantilever slabs on either side was David Lee. A highly talented engineer, he joined the firm in 1956. He gained an international reputation as well as many international awards for his work with prestressed concrete. He lectured widely, wrote several books on bridge and structure design (notably The Theory of Bearings & Expansion Joints for Bridges in 1971), and became a visiting professor at both Imperial College in London and Newcastle University. Elected President of the Institution of Structural Engineers in 1985, he received the CBE in 1989. He became a partner in the firm in 1966 and succeeded John Baxter as managing partner in 1978.

More staff were recruited to cope with the growing number of major projects. Among the newcomers in 1962 were two civil engineers with experience from the construction industry.

Although Maunsell in the UK did not carry out many building schemes, one of the few that it did complete, the rail maintenance depot at Paddington in London (1968), was a prize-winning design and was later declared to be a building of national importance.

Dudley New, who became a partner, had been chief engineer with the construction company, Holland Hannen & Cubitts; David Hook came from the same firm as a senior engineer, becoming a partner in 1968. Few staff left; often those who did soon rejoined. There were many reasons for this - the quality of the staff – John Baxter had a deserved reputation for picking good people – the friendly, open and transparent working environment, the exciting and innovative projects, the early opportunities to exercise responsibility. Fundamentally, staff at every level were well looked after.

One of the few major maritime projects of this period was the reconstruction of the dockyard in Malta, completed in 1966. Maunsell's skill and ingenuity was demonstrated here through the conception of a flap dock gate incorporating air tanks, which could be pumped out or flooded to raise and lower it. Although the design was patented, it did not bring in much work.

By the late 1960s three-quarters of the staff in London were working on Westway. The firm was too dependent on major highways projects but attempts to win other types of work had met only with limited success. Despite Guy Maunsell's reputation for maritime work, the firm had secured only two minor projects, for dry docks in South Shields and Swansea. The firm also lacked the expertise to make much of an impact in the buildings sector; the firm's only major building was the prize-winning Paddington rail maintenance depot in London in 1968, which was later listed as a building of national importance. There was one tunnel – the firm carried out a feasibility study on the Mount Bingham Tunnel for the States of Jersey in 1962 and was involved in the supervision of its construction five years later. Some suspect that the UK firm's inability to diversify within the UK owed something to a reluctance on the part of John Baxter and his senior London colleagues to chase work and promote the firm in the same way Miles Birkett was doing in Australia. Marketing was still a dirty word in the UK civil engineering consulting profession.

This also seems to have been a barrier to establishing much of an overseas presence outside Australia. In the Middle East, an attempt to establish an office in Libya in 1965 came to nothing. A joint venture was formed by the firm in South Africa in 1969. UK staff were seconded to the new firm in an attempt to exploit the firm's expertise in bridges. A number of important bridges were designed and built but South Africa during apartheid was an uneasy place in which to work and Maunsell withdrew after a few years.

In the Far East, a foray into Thailand in the late 1960s did not initially bear fruit although contact was made with Sindhu Pulsirivong, a well-respected consulting engineer specialising in building structures. Combining this skill with Maunsell's expertise in roads and ports, a successful office was established. Also in 1969 the firm opened an office in Singapore in association with J D & D M Watson, consulting engineers in public health, sewerage and water. Stemming from this, the firm was commissioned by the Ministry of Overseas Development in the UK to carry out a design study in association with the Singapore government for a 500,000 ton capacity dry dock at Sembawang. The radical design, using Maunsell's air-operated flap gates for the dry dock, the largest in South East Asia, enabled huge savings to be made, continuing the firm's commitment to saving time and money for client and contractor. The work was completed in 1975 by which time prospects for the firm in the Far East had completely changed. The Sembawang dockyard was a typical example of the major projects being funded by wealthier, developed nations or through international development banks.

As industrialisation marched hand in hand with population growth, the region's expanding cities needed improved infrastructure, transport and housing as the flow of people, goods and communications increased. Singapore, which became independent of Malaysia in 1965, was among the earliest countries to establish export-led light industries. It became one of the region's greatest economic success stories, second only to Japan in growth per head, ranking alongside Hong Kong, Taiwan and South Korea as one of South East Asia's 'four little dragons'. Thailand, although it would eventually rank second only to Singapore in its average rate of post-war growth, was ten years behind. It was still too poor to generate the interest in major development projects from international sponsors. But it was an area full of potential and Maunsell would make the most of this during the next decade.

Maunsell in Australia

Maunsell's work on the Narrows Bridge and Tasman Bridge made all the difference to the firm's parlous early finances. These bridges also made the reputation of G Maunsell & Partners in Australia. With expertise in the use of prestressed concrete in short supply in Australia plus a refreshingly down-to-earth approach so different from so many other British consulting engineers, the firm was well-placed to make the most of the country's post-war economic boom.

Australia was embarking upon an extraordinary period of growth. Between the late 1940s and the early 1970s the population doubled and economic activity tripled. The Liberal government of Robert Menzies was committed to a strong public sector but also fostered private enterprise and abolished restrictions on foreign investment. Domestic industry flourished under a regime of import quotas and tariffs. Menzies encouraged Australians 'to think in a big way, to be thankful for big things, to be proud of big enterprises'.

This fusion of a strong public sector with thriving private enterprise completely transformed the way major construction projects were dealt with in Australia. Previously they had been designed and built by the public works departments in individual States. During the 1950s these organisations were faced with the same challenge as their counterparts in the UK – the need to develop a more extensive infrastructure to accommodate the growth in mobility stemming from rising prosperity. They tackled it by commissioning designs from consulting civil engineers and awarding tenders for construction to private contractors.

Developments in prestressed concrete and precasting led to significant reductions in erection costs, producing an overall cost advantage compared with steel. Engineers appreciated the way in which the material could be used to create elegant designs, which contributed to the landscape setting of the structure. As car ownership grew and the population of Australia's major cities expanded – Sydney, for instance, exceeded two million in the late 1950s – it was clear that improvements were needed to the transport infrastructure. In many cases, this meant constructing new bridges over significant expanses of water where large spans and high clearances were necessary for the passage of shipping.

The Narrows Bridge and Tasman Bridge were typical examples of such projects. The Narrows Bridge, completed in 1960, was included in Western Australia's heritage list in 1999 because of its innovative design. A beautiful, pioneering structure, it was created with regard for its setting, impressed the client and demonstrated to the State authorities just how effectively the consulting engineer and contractor could work together. It was on this bridge that the Australian firm applied the pioneering Gambia piles developed by the firm several years earlier. On the Narrows Bridge, the piles for the foundations were driven 46 metres using a drop-hammer acting inside the casing.

The firm's creative, innovative and adventurous approach to prestressed concrete had already attracted a brilliant young engineering graduate, Geoff Fernie, who became the first Australian employee of the firm in 1957. Shortly afterwards, he was joined on the Narrows Bridge site by Geoff Bingham who had been sent from London as resident site engineer. This was the first example of one of the firm's most enduring characteristics. The expansion of the firm throughout the world would be based partly on the development of the potential of local talented engineers allied to the existing skills of Maunsell engineers from other countries.

In the days before developments in technology and travel shrank the world and transformed long-distance communications, it was clear that major projects like the Narrows Bridge could not be properly managed from as far away as London. Telephone links were rudimentary, telegrams inadequate for the transmission of technical information, long-distance air travel in its infancy. Miles Birkett, who had travelled abroad with Guy Maunsell, believed that the firm needed a permanent presence in Australia. Scarcely had work on the Narrows Bridge begun before he had proposed that an office should be opened. His colleagues agreed and Birkett was despatched to Australia.

The contribution of Miles Birkett to the success of the Australian firm cannot be underestimated. Those engineers who joined the firm under his leadership hold him in the highest regard. The UK partners had chosen the right man to open up the market. A gregarious, genial and kindly man, whose personality made it easy for him to develop an ever-widening circle of contacts, he used up his immense reserves of energy in pursuit of the firm's success. He insisted upon the highest standards of design and construction. This was something he brought with him from the UK firm but in Australia it influenced the whole profession. The new way of doing things caused some resistance from contractors who, ignorant of the Maunsell ethos, kicked against what they regarded as interference from consulting engineers on how they should construct projects.

But they came to appreciate that the firm was among the more sympathetic consultants while Birkett's stance on quality found favour with clients.

Birkett also shared the commercial instincts of the firm's founder, a characteristic rare at the time in civil engineers. Rather than thinking just about engineering structures, Birkett was talking and thinking about client relationships, marketing and promotion. In Geoff Fernie's words, Birkett 'played a deeper game'. With his leadership ability and organisational skills, he gave the firm a leading edge among its local rivals. The success of this British outsider created resentment among some Australian rivals even though Birkett was showing them opportunities they had never realised were there. The irony is that Birkett probably would not have been able to exercise his marketing flair in the UK where the profession still frowned on such activities.

From the time he arrived in Australia, Miles Birkett had a vision of G Maunsell & Partners as a national firm. He shrewdly realised that if the firm was to capitalise upon the two major projects it had in hand in this exciting new market, the office needed to be at the heart of Australian commercial and political life. Canberra, the national capital, remained under-developed; political and financial influence still resided in Melbourne. Here the first Australian office was opened in June 1957. There were three staff – Birkett, Dudley Sewell, another of Maunsell's original team, and a secretary, Barbara Mapstone.

But Birkett also knew that in a country the size of Australia one office would not be enough. He recognised the importance of being represented throughout the country and realised that the States themselves were economic powerhouses. Until the firm was properly established and other offices could be set up, Birkett constantly criss-crossed the country. He grew to hate flying, eventually abandoning the airplane for internal travel in favour of the railway, even though this took much longer and often left him waiting in remote locations at unearthly hours for someone to collect him. Eventually offices were opened in Melbourne, Canberra, Perth and Sydney. The firm grew from seven staff to 250 in ten years. Pat Hughes, who joined the Australian office in 1960, later recorded that 'all this was basically Miles's creation, all guided and directed by his original scheming and with the many difficulties overcome with dogged perseverance'.

Dudley Sewell returned to London early in 1959 but his transfer had established a pattern of traffic between the two offices that was not all one way. Just as UK engineers travelled to Australia, Australian engineers were also sent to the UK. The growth of Maunsell in Australia was attributable not just to the expanding volume of work but also to this generous policy of developing the skills of young Australian engineers by sending them to the London office. Throughout the 1960s the relationship between the two parts of the firm was excellent. There was always rivalry (mainly focused on the varying cricketing fortunes of each nation) but there was also genuine friendship. The relationship was characterised by John Laurie, who joined the firm in 1959, as that of 'a son growing up'.

In fact, the first Australian to be employed in London was Steve Cowie, in 1958, who was only transferred to the Melbourne office a year later. The first Australian to be seconded to London was Geoff Fernie in June 1960. He stayed for more than two years, inspired by Peter Stott and David Lee, and found that 'London staff were marvellously considerate; an Australian remained a novelty then. The experience converted me to a state of ease with English ways'. He was followed shortly afterwards by John Laurie and Jim Leslie, who later played major roles within the firm in Australia. Laurie had spent four years with the Dominion Bridge Company in Canada and wanted to continue with bridge engineering on his return to Australia. He wrote to Miles Birkett who offered him a job. Laurie joined the Melbourne office in January 1959, followed a year later by Jim Leslie, one of whose first jobs was as a site engineer on the Narrows Bridge.

As the Narrows Bridge was being completed, construction of the 1,300 metre long Tasman Bridge finally began. In driving piles for the foundations some 79 metres deep, then some of the deepest foundations of their type in the world, the firm built on the experience of the Narrows Bridge. The piles were bored by oscillation and grabbing and the firm later adapted this technology for the complex foundation cylinders of the West Gate Bridge in Melbourne. Completed in 1964, the Tasman Bridge was designed not just to facilitate navigation but also to ensure that if a ship struck any one of the piers, the adjoining piers would not collapse like falling dominoes. A practical demonstration of the effectiveness of the design was given in January 1975. A ship under a drunken skipper collided with the bridge. Two piers were destroyed but the remainder were unaffected. Jim Leslie was involved with the ensuing restoration work.

The design of the Tasman Bridge was principally the work of John Baxter and Peter Stott. Guy Maunsell's own preference was not for prestressed concrete but for steel girders. He was convinced that steel was easier and cheaper for the contractor to use. He felt that his views had been ignored by his younger partners and he cited their failure to consult him as one of the reasons for stepping down from the partnership in February 1959. The minutes of the management committee meeting record that Maunsell felt 'he had not been consulted in the early stages about the design for this project ... he completely disagreed with the ideas put forward by Mr

The Tasman Bridge, completed in 1964, was widely regarded as the structure that reclaimed for British civil engineering international eminence in prestressed concrete structures.

The elegant Gladesville bridge, completed in 1964, was the last design to which Guy Maunsell contributed before his death. It was the largest concrete arch span bridge in the world at the time.

The Batman Bridge in Tasmania, completed in 1968, was Australia's first cable-stayed steel bridge.

Stott and Mr Baxter; he thought it was unsound and not the best for the client or contractor ... he felt very strongly that his idea was the right one. He felt he had met with obstinacy in this matter and it was one of the reasons why he felt that he must now retire'. In fact, the Tasman Bridge was commonly acknowledged to have wrested back for Britain the lead lost to the French during the inter-war years in the design of major prestressed concrete structures.

This 150 metre high water jet in the central lakes area was opened in 1970 as part of Australia's bicentennial celebrations. Visible in the background is the Commonwealth Avenue Bridge. Maunsell was consulting engineer for much of the road, bridge and other works in the central area of Canberra, Australia's national capital, from the early 1960s to the late 1980s.

Guy Maunsell's last major contribution to the design of prestressed concrete structures was the elegant bridge at Gladesville in Sydney. He made his initial sketches for the concept of the Bridge while standing on the shores of Sydney Harbour. The great French engineer and pioneer of prestressed concrete design, Eugene Freyssinet, was also consulted by the firm on the design of the bridge. Neither he nor Guy Maunsell lived to see it completed. Construction work began in 1960, the year before Maunsell's death. Commissioned by an Anglo-Australian consortium of contractors, the six-lane 580 metre long bridge was carried on a central arch 305 metres in length, making it the largest concrete span in the world when it was finished in 1964. Maunsell's concept was an alternative to the original proposed by the

Commissioner of Main Roads for New South Wales for a steel girder bridge over the upper reaches of Sydney Harbour which would inevitably have drawn invidious comparisons with the majestic Sydney Harbour Bridge. The arch was formed by a series of precast box sections, which were set in place and, having been jointed together, lifted off the formwork using Freyssinet flat jacks, the first time this had ever been done in such a situation. Another advance was that the Huntley's Point overpass, on the approaches to the bridge, was one of the first projects to include computer-based calculations. Maunsell and his colleagues succeeded in creating a design which was not only technically advanced but also individual and beautiful in its own right. It was one of his most outstanding achievements. John Baxter was one of those closely associated with Gladesville – in later years he liked to point out that Gladesville was an early example of a Design & Construct contract.

By the time of Guy Maunsell's death, he had made the firm the leading designer of prestressed concrete bridges in Australia. Thanks to this success, many other bridge commissions followed. Among the most notable were the King's Avenue and Commonwealth Avenue Bridges, completed in 1962-64, which formed part of the development of Canberra for the National Capital Development Commission (NCDC). Another innovation was the Batman Bridge over the Lower Tamar in Tasmania, the first cable-stayed steel bridge in Australia, completed in 1968. It was the first bridge in the world to incorporate a single inclined tower.

Work in Canberra formed an important part of the firm's business between 1959 and 1988. The revival of the development of the Australian national capital to the designs completed before the First World War by Walter Burley Griffin was due more than anyone else to prime minister Robert Menzies. G Maunsell & Partners' links with Canberra began in 1959, thanks partly to Miles Birkett's persuasive powers and partly to the relationship which the firm had developed over the years with William Holford & Partners, the main planning consultants for the entire project.

The Australian office developed a close working relationship with the client, the powerful and professional NCDC. In 1972 this would lead Clive Price, who had been Engineering Commissioner at the NCDC, to join the firm, taking over the Canberra office. Through this close relationship, Maunsell became principal consultant for many of Canberra's major infrastructure works. As well as the two bridges, the firm also designed the 150 metre high Captain Cook Memorial Fountain (1970) and the roads and bridges surrounding New Parliament House (1988). All this work was not only a source of great pride within the firm; Miles Birkett also used the Canberra office, opened in 1960, as a de facto training ground for many of those who later became leading figures in the firm. The Australian office, through its growing reputation, was attracting talented young engineers. In a young firm run by young people (Birkett turned 40 in 1966), there was an informal atmosphere but one suffused with a spirit which came from sharing pioneering experiences.

Although work in Canberra was prestigious, it did little to widen the scope of Maunsell in Australia. Miles Birkett was aware that reliance on bridge design with its very slim financial margins was not the basis for financial stability. He was determined to use his marketing skills to expand the range of work carried out by the firm. There had already been a successful attempt to capitalise on the reputation of Guy Maunsell and the UK firm for maritime work. In 1959 the firm undertook a port study for Derby in Western Australia. Then, in 1960, Pat Hughes joined the Melbourne office. An experienced port engineer who had been Chief Engineer at the port of Portland in Victoria, he steadily won more maritime work for the firm. The advent of containerisation required the speedy modernisation of the country's port facilities and specialised ports were needed to handle the increasing volume of mineral exports. Early projects included a bulk tanker terminal at Westernport in Victoria (1966) and the container terminals in Brisbane (1969) and Sydney (1970) as well as several further studies for new deep ports and mining ports.

Miles Birkett never let a commercial opportunity slip past. He was imbued with the 'can do' spirit typical of the firm's founder. In 1961, he clinched a major new contract to design and supervise the construction of the biggest development in Australian railways since the completion of the Trans-Continental Railway nearly 50 years earlier. The purpose of the Western Australia Standard Gauge Project was the standardisation of the gauge over a line that stretched 724 kilometres. As well as new track, it encompassed the design of new marshalling yards, depots, stations and maintenance facilities. A complex project, eventually let in more than 120 separate contracts, it was intended to assist the exploitation of iron ore and to carry iron ore and wheat to the ports. It kept Maunsell busy for almost a decade, providing financial stability, developing new skills, and attracting talented new staff. Paul Andrew was sent out from London to assist Birkett in opening an office in Perth in 1962. He was supposed to return to the UK after three months but he became a partner and stayed in Australia until his retirement in 1985.

The remarkable thing was that Maunsell had very limited experience in railways. Miles Birkett was in Perth to see work on the Narrows Bridge when he heard rumours about the Standard Gauge Project. Demonstrating his sharp commercial instincts, he immediately arranged to see the State's Commissioner of Railways and, based on little more than tackling the design of 100 kilometres of railway over difficult terrain in Iraq, talked the Commissioner into awarding Maunsell the work. He was helped by the Narrows Bridge that had impressed the State premier as a successful example of private enterprise where consulting engineer and contractor worked well alongside each other. Birkett only thought about the practical implications once he had won the contract. The episode illustrated perfectly what John Laurie described as the 'persuasive and audacious' side of Birkett's character.

Birkett rang John Baxter in London who arranged the secondment of Pat Sands from the UK Railway Advisory Service. Sands was sent out to Australia as the senior technical advisor on the project, stayed on and became a partner. Reserved, courteous and respected, he was the rock on which the firm developed its reputation for railway projects in Australia and subsequently worldwide. Once again the transfer of skilled personnel from one place to another, emerging from the close relationship between Maunsell in Australia and the UK, played a central part in the firm's expansion.

In its early years the Australian office relied on the London office not just for design capacity. It also benefited from the UK's adoption of modern technology. In many firms slide-rules, logarithms and trigonometric tables were still the standard tools used for engineering computations. Slow, noisy mechanical calculators appeared but were quickly replaced with electronic machines, although these too were limited in function. The Melbourne office began to use computer bureaux, took advantage of the software developed in London and, by the late 1960s, had acquired its first in-house computer. Geoff Tickell moved from London to Melbourne and helped to develop software and computer use.

As the firm matured, as engineers enhanced their skills and expanded in confidence with a greater body of work, as the Australian office assumed more and more responsibility for its own contracts, the question of greater independence for Maunsell in Australia inevitably arose. There was also growing pressure in Australia for work to be given to independent Australian consulting engineers. Although almost all Maunsell's staff were Australian, this did not stop jealous and resentful rivals from portraying the firm as the branch of a UK partnership. Miles Birkett first raised the idea of independence in 1962 but it was not until 18 June 1965 that a separate Australian partnership was formed as Maunsell & Partners. The firms also agreed on their respective spheres of influence – the UK would cover the UK, Europe and the Middle East, Australian would cover Australia, Asia and the Pacific. This was not intended to be a rigid demarcation; that would have gone against the grain of the firm's overarching philosophy.

A few years later this division of spheres of influence was formalised. The firm successfully sought the agreement of the Association of Consulting Engineers of Australia (ACEA) to become a limited company. Although this was opposed by the more conservative equivalent body in the UK, Maunsell's UK partners willingly agreed to the incorporation of the Australian firm in 1970. In Australia 79 per cent of Maunsell & Partners Pty Ltd was owned by the Australian partners; the remainder was owned by another company, Maunsell Pty Ltd. This company, owned half by the Australian partners and half by the UK partners, owned a similar proportion of G Maunsell & Partners in London.

As a result of this, Maunsell Consultants was formed, made up of equal numbers of partners from the UK and Australia, to cover Maunsell's work in the rest of the world. It was through Maunsell Consultants that the firm would make a major breakthrough in South East Asia. But the new firm also had another purpose. Bearing in mind Guy Maunsell's emphasis on the importance of unity, it was also designed to preserve the links between the firms in the UK and Australia after the latter's independence.

Before any breakthrough came in South East Asia, however, the momentum powering the progress of Maunsell in Australia came to a grinding halt. Economic growth in Melbourne had encouraged a consortium of local businesses to form the Lower Yarra Crossing Authority (LYCA) in 1964. The LYCA pressed for the construction of a major bridge over the Yarra to link the two sides of the city to improve east-west access and remove barriers to further development. With Maunsell's reputation for big bridges in Australia, the firm was asked to prepare a preliminary report for the LYCA on the feasibility of constructing a bridge across the river. In 1967 Maunsell, with Freeman Fox & Partners, a London practice with a worldwide reputation for major steel bridges, were appointed as joint consulting engineers for what became known as the West Gate Bridge. Maunsell was responsible for the design and supervision of construction of the massive concrete approach spans and foundations, Freeman Fox for the five main steel spans.

At ten minutes to twelve on the morning of 15 October 1970, the 112 metre long steel span between piers 10 and 11 suddenly collapsed, killing 35 men and injuring many more. One engineer in Maunsell's Melbourne office had gone up to the roof for a cigarette but returned ashen-faced to say that he couldn't see the bridge. On the afternoon of the collapse, as the dead and injured were being carried away, with smoke still rising from the scene, Miles Birkett returned to the office with Geoff Fernie, by now a partner, and told him 'That's the end of 14 years' work in Australia'.

It was the most serious industrial accident in Australia history. By the end of the month, a Royal Commission had been formed to investigate the accident. It sat for nearly eight months. During that time, the resources of Maunsell in Australia were almost entirely absorbed by the Royal Commission. Miles Birkett, as chairman and managing director, attended every day. It broke the morale not just of those who were involved with the Commission; everyone in the company was affected by this lengthy period of uncertainty. Geoff Fernie remembers how he was 'crucified' on the stand by the lawyers.

Throughout the hearings, the Commission was assisted by the detailed personal diaries kept by Baikie James. He was famous for stating matters as they really were and always kept meticulous diaries. These proved to be of incalculable value when matters of fact needed to be established. At the conclusion of the hearings, the Commission complimented Baikie James on the detail and frankness of his diaries.

The Report presented by the Commission makes appalling reading. The ultimate cause of what the Commission described as an 'utterly unnecessary' and 'inexcusable' tragedy was the removal of a series of transverse bolts from the spans in order to relieve a bulge in the steelwork. The underlying causes of the collapse were much more extensive. The Report lists the difficult relations between the consulting engineers and contractors, the lax approach towards design and calculations and poor supervision of the project by Freeman Fox, the inadequate experience of engineers assigned to the project, and a whole catalogue of other errors which cumulatively led up to the disaster.

No one, neither the LYCA nor the consultants, contractors or trades unions, emerged from the tragedy without criticism. Miles Birkett was criticised for failing to do more to persuade Freeman Fox to improve its relationship with the contractors. Paul Andrew believes that Birkett was placed in a very difficult position. He lacked experience in the design of steel bridges which immediately put him at a disadvantage with the Freeman Fox partners, who, in any case, were also older and more aloof. Maunsell, with Freeman Fox, was also criticised for responding to the concerns of the contractors over the safety of the structure by giving a categorical assurance that 'the bridge design is fully adequate during all stages of erection'. This, reported the Commission, was unjustified, unsupported by sufficient calculations, improper and in breach of the duty of the joint consultants to the LYCA, the contractor and the workforce.

But 'the greater part of the blame' was placed by the Commission on Freeman Fox which was condemned as negligent in relation to the structural design and the safety of the construction methods. Maunsell's technical work, on the other hand, was judged to be 'highly satisfactory'. This verdict was supported by the testimony of the general manager of the LYCA, which turned out to be crucial in sustaining the confidence of Australian clients in Maunsell's technical capacity. The report highlighted the distinction between the way in which the two firms operated. The Commission pointed out that in Australia consulting engineers frequently worked out erection procedures as part of the pre-tender design, permitting contractors to vary these, provided the variations were demonstrably safe. This, the Commission noted, was the reverse of how British consultants worked. Maunsell, of course, was an exception in the UK. The Commission reported that 'the West Gate Bridge exemplifies this difference very well. For the prestressed concrete approach spans designed by Maunsell, the erection procedures were fully specified and detailed. The successful tenderer ... put forward a few modifications and these were subsequently approved by Maunsell. On the other hand, [Freeman Fox] left the tenderers a free hand so far as erection procedures were concerned'.

Although the Commission cleared Maunsell, the firm, as joint consultants, had to be dismissed along with Freeman Fox. Maunsell was re-appointed a few days later but the damaging publicity of the earlier decision made a lasting impression. The firm almost certainly lost the work for the proposed Melbourne underground rail loop because the appointment would have been politically inappropriate. Geoff Fernie's health was seriously affected by the episode. Miles Birkett, already ill with cancer, was a broken man. He never recovered and died aged only 45 less than a year after the conclusion of the Royal Commission. Pat Hughes later wrote that 'there were many times in these dark days when many of us felt that he should be more outspoken in his own defence; that he should ward off the tacit accusations of his complicity and lack of omniscience. But he wouldn't move from his chosen course which was to avoid hurting anybody who was going through the same bitter mill with himself. Further, he insisted on bearing the brunt of the attacks on his position as though he alone of his firm was implicated'.

The episode had, John Laurie recalled, a 'crushing' effect on the Australian firm. 'It was only with great difficulty', recalled Paul Andrew, 'that we clawed our way back.' Between the collapse of the bridge in October 1970 and the death of Birkett in June 1972, Maunsell in Australia, Laurie believes, 'slowly ran out of gas'. But there was, says Geoff Fernie, 'a sense that we were going to meet the challenge'. In Australia this was initially achieved through the leadership of John Laurie. But it was also inextricably linked to the firm's development in South East Asia.

The West Gate Bridge was a difficult project for Maunsell because of the collapse of one of the steel spans. However, the concrete approaches, which Maunsell designed, were problem-free and, as this image illustrates, a striking example of modern concrete box girder design.

Part 3
1970-1989

The Growth of Maunsell Worldwide

It was during the 1970s and the 1980s that Maunsell began to emerge as an international group. The key to this expansion was the enormous success of the firm's operations in Iraq but particularly in Hong Kong. John Downer, the Australian who was in charge of Hong Kong's operations from the outset in 1970, had spent time with the firm in the UK and understood its capabilities. He also possessed the commercial flair that Miles Birkett had deployed so well in Australia. In addition, he was adept, as were both Guy Maunsell and Birkett, in building up networks of influential contacts. In a region where massive investment was taking place, these business skills, combined with the firm's established reputation, proved a winning formula. From a standing start, Maunsell became one of the leading civil engineering consultancies in Hong Kong within a decade.

The Maunsell firms in the UK and Australia supported the development of this new venture by repeating the pattern that had proved so successful in Australia. Hong Kong benefited from their mutual support and co-operation. The firms in the UK and Australia seconded some of their finest engineers to Hong Kong while others were employed on design work in their home countries. While reliance on Maunsell in the UK for technical leadership had considerable benefits for the Group's expansion, it was undoubtedly detrimental to the development of business in the UK. At the same time, the firm in Hong Kong recruited and trained local staff who within a few years were taking leading roles in the new business. By the 1980s, the Hong Kong firm was seeking to achieve the same results in the newly opened Chinese market.

Through Downer's financial acumen, the Hong Kong firm became the most profitable part of Maunsell. The work provided by Hong Kong for Maunsell in Australia and the UK helped to sustain their businesses during times when their local economies were in difficulties. But some of the ways in which Maunsell grew in Hong Kong were also being explored simultaneously by the Australian and UK firms. In Hong Kong, where the pace of investment in infrastructure projects was frenetic, the firm had learned to meet deadlines and budgets by balancing engineering professionalism with the needs of the client. Here it was the needs of the client, rather than the professional pride of the engineer, which was the driving force behind the acquisition of new skills. As Maunsell in Australia rebuilt its morale in the aftermath of the West Gate Bridge disaster, it too diversified by turning to previously unexplored areas of work, notably environmental management. In the UK, the firm broke into the Middle East market and, through major projects in Iraq in particular, learned the lessons of meeting the needs of the client through adhering to deadlines and financial targets. The UK firm also took advantage of the reputation for rail and mass transit developed by Maunsell in Hong Kong to undertake several similar large-scale projects. At the same time, all around the world, Maunsell sustained the firm's reputation for innovative design and pioneering new techniques. All this placed the firm in the world's top 25 civil engineering consultancies.

The firm as a whole managed to adapt to the changes taking place in the market. Clients, for example, began to favour consulting engineers who could provide a comprehensive service. This, in any case, was a natural path for Maunsell. Guy Maunsell himself had never wanted to be a narrow specialist. The ethos of the firm was to take up the challenges provided by a wide variety of engineering projects. So diversification was an obvious way for Maunsell to meet this trend. Another was by joining with other consultants who offered services Maunsell did not possess. As a result, the firm took part in several projects with other consultants around the world. In Australia and the UK, Maunsell for the first time acquired other engineering consultancies to benefit from their additional skills. Fee competition was another trend, beginning in Australia in the late 1960s, then spreading to the UK and eventually to Hong Kong. It was a development generally disliked by the profession but one that Maunsell was equipped to deal with, thanks to its growing commercial skills.

One hindrance to the corporate growth of the firm regionally and internationally was the continuing partnership culture. By the late 1980s, each of the three firms had become a limited liability company. Yet even in Australia, where this had occurred in 1970, let alone the UK, where the profession was much more conservative, the firm never quite succeeded in making the transition from partnership to corporate governance. It was common practice for the best engineers in the firm to assume leading managerial roles when in other sectors many of these roles would have been filled with specialists. So the firms in Australia and the UK never really got to grips with the financial management of the business. This problem was compounded in the UK because, unlike the firms in Australia and Hong Kong, the firm was slow to appreciate the crucial value of marketing. This made it more difficult for the UK firm to meet the new commercial challenges arising in a changing market place. In Hong Kong, however, where an entrepreneurial culture was much more widespread, the firm's business skills were much sharper and this showed in its record of financial success.

The varying speed with which different parts of the firm around the world grasped the need to develop a more business-like approach also held back the corporate development of the business as an international group. By the late 1980s it was clear that Maunsell was not operating as a coherent international business. For each of the three firms, local and regional interests were a greater priority. All this had to change if Maunsell was to capitalise on the firm's obvious potential for further expansion.

9

Maunsell in Hong Kong

The Sembawang dry dock, with its innovative air-operated flap gates, was built for the Singapore government between 1968 and 1975. It was the largest dry dock in the world.

In 1970 the responsibility of establishing overseas subsidiaries was given to Maunsell Consultants, a partnership made up of partners from the UK and Australian firms. The first of these was Maunsell Consultants Asia (MCA), also formed in 1970. It was not really a new venture, more the formalisation of an operation which had already begun.

The Sembawang dry dock project, started in 1968, demonstrated the opportunities available in South East Asia. But to make the most of these something more organised was needed than waiting for the occasional aid project to come along. The firm had to have someone on the ground, opening up the market. It was decided to start in Singapore where the firm already had contacts. When Miles Birkett asked Geoff Fernie who to send, Fernie told him without hesitation that John Downer should be the man to go. Birkett said 'I hoped you would say that. He's the man I've chosen.' Downer, urbane, respected, commercially minded, had joined the firm in 1963. He had worked in the UK and in Australia so he knew both sides of the business. Given a deliberately vague brief, he was eager to go. At the airport, Birkett said to him, 'We'll give you three years. Don't worry if you don't succeed – you don't cost very much'.

Downer arrived in Singapore early in 1969 and began travelling widely throughout Asia in search of work. Very quickly the firm was short-listed for a project in Taiwan. On the way there, Downer stopped in Hong Kong. The ACEA viewed the British Colony as a small market already well-covered by established British consulting engineers. Downer, though, found Hong Kong was a revelation. The encouraging reception he was given by the Colony's Director of Engineering Development made him realise just how much potential there was.

Downer quickly decided that Hong Kong rather than Singapore should be the base for MCA and he moved there early in 1970. In the words of David Odgers, then a young Australian engineer, later chief executive of Maunsell's worldwide operations, 'this was the happiest of circumstances - the right man in the right place at the right time'. The Colony was ready for massive development. Hong Kong's population had risen by one million people in a decade. The housing they lived in was totally inadequate, the existing infrastructure, including highways and transportation, could no longer cope.

Shortly after Downer's arrival in Hong Kong, a new Governor was appointed. Sir Murray Maclehose took up his post in November 1971. He quickly identified his priorities – water and power, education, healthcare and housing – and embarked on a major development programme. These were essential, as refugees fleeing the turmoil of China's civil war had swelled Hong Kong's population. By this time it was clear that they were not going to return and they needed to be looked after. In the words of Hong Kong's historian, Frank Welsh, the development programme included 'the reconstruction of a transport system, rehousing half the population, and providing acceptable levels of education and healthcare'. Between 1970 and 1972 government spending increased by 50 per cent.

Maunsell was in an excellent position to take advantage of this remarkable boom. Although the firm had emerged almost blameless from the West Gate Bridge disaster, some rivals did attempt to tarnish the Maunsell reputation through guilt by association; but potential clients could see beyond this to the wider reputation the firm had earned from its work on prestressed concrete structures and from highways and transportation schemes in the UK and Australia. Hong Kong officials also appreciated the less formal, less starchy approach of the firm compared with some of its well-established rivals both in Hong Kong and in the UK. While the first meeting arranged by principals of other firms attempting to break into the market was almost always at the highest level in government, John Downer took a different approach. He developed strong relationships with officials at every appropriate level since he knew that they would be promoted to positions of increasing influence. It also helped that, as Maunsell expanded in Hong Kong, more senior staff were Chinese, communicating directly with their Chinese counterparts in government departments. The firm was ahead of the competition in developing this network, which proved invaluable in obtaining a feel for the market and the needs of clients.

The Route 4 expressway along the Kowloon foothills, completed in 1976, was Maunsell's first project in Hong Kong.

Maunsell's first appointment in Hong Kong was as consulting engineer to the Highways Office of the Hong Kong Public Works Department for the 8 kilometre long Route 4 expressway along the Kowloon foothills. The staff magazine, *The Maunsell Whisper*, begun in 1970 to connect the separate parts of the expanding firm, reported that, 'Wholly within the New Territories, leased from China until 1997, Route 4, at HK$100 million, could be Maunsell's greatest gift to Mao. Or with ping-pong diplomacy at its best, perhaps a Peking office will be next!' Route 4 not only brought a flavour of future projects but also set the pattern of co-operation in Hong Kong between the Australian and UK firms while Maunsell established itself in the Colony. The partners employed the strategy that had helped to establish the firm in Australia. So Route 4 was designed in London and Melbourne and experienced British and Australian engineers were sent to Hong Kong.

Among them was Reg Thomas, a down-to-earth Welshman who had been chief resident engineer on Westway. He took up the same post for Route 4. His great skill as a manager was in team building and he played a major part in creating a corporate spirit in a fledgling organisation. He spent many years in Hong Kong, working on a string of major projects. There were several Australians, including Ian Brewster, who worked in the office managing the construction contracts, fellow engineer Bill Kelly and Barry Guildford, the guiding draughtsman in the Hong Kong office. With a view to winning more highway work, Peter Gray, a UK traffic engineer, joined the team in 1971 and produced feasibility studies that were later to provide a constant flow of work for the firm. In early 1973 it was decided that Hong Kong had to build a local design capability and this responsibility was given to Richard Garrett who was seconded from the UK. He eventually became a director and saw the Hong Kong design office become the largest within Maunsell.

At the same time the Hong Kong firm began employing Chinese staff straightaway – the first were secretary Rose Yu and draughtsman Karl Yip - and within five years several of them were occupying senior management positions. The firm's policy of employing and developing the potential of local staff as part of its strategy of breaking into the market set it apart from long-established British firms in Hong Kong.

One of the earliest highway projects was the road from Happy Valley to Aberdeen. This included the Canal Road Flyover, an urban elevated highway, in Happy Valley, and the Aberdeen Tunnel, with the Wong Chuk Hang interchange at the Aberdeen end. The Flyover was designed using the U-beam, another Maunsell innovation. Conceived by David Lee, it had been developed in the UK as a standard precast, pretensioned beam. Since there were no precasting factories in Hong Kong, the design had to be modified to use post-tensioning. In that form it became a standard beam in Hong Kong.

The Aberdeen Tunnel was another project for which Maunsell had little relevant experience. Apart from the small tunnel in Jersey, it was the first major road tunnel through rock designed by the firm. It was tackled in the usual Maunsell way. Specialist consultants were hired and passed on their own expertise by working alongside Maunsell's own staff. The firm seconded another engineer from Australia, Mike Millar, to oversee this project and he later went on to head the firm's geotechnical arm. Other road tunnels followed and Maunsell became a world leader in tunnel design.

Less than three years after Maunsell opened its office next to a live snake shop in Kowloon, the firm had 17 projects in hand worth HK$1200 million. The number of staff had grown to 105 but only nine of the 35 office staff and 14 of the 70 staff on site were expatriates. As the firm's newsletter remarked, 'our own rapidly rising involvement reflects the Colony's general developing pace'.

'Rebuilding in Hong Kong,' wrote Frank Welsh, 'proceeded at an uncomfortable pace.' In October 1972 Maclehose announced an ambitious ten year urban development programme to house nearly two million people. Most of this would be achieved by the creation of the New Towns, a network of balanced and free-standing settlements in the New Territories to replace deteriorating, declining and overcrowded suburbs.

Sha Tin was one of the first of these New Towns, designed to house half a million people in an improved environment within a decade. Maunsell was initially appointed to carry out the infrastructure works for Stage 1 of Sha Tin New Town for the New Territories Development Department of the Public Works Department. The appointment of the firm for Stage 2 quickly followed. While work began in September 1973 and peaked in the 1980s, when Maunsell had 180 staff on site, the firm was still working on the development of Sha Tin in 2005 under the original 1973 agreement. The first partner in charge was Peter Gray, who had joined Maunsell in the UK in 1965 and was sent out to Hong Kong in 1971. One of the new recruits to the firm's expanding Sha Tin office in January 1975 was an experienced engineer, Francis Bong. A graduate of Hong Kong University who had spent several years in Canada, Bong would later take over the running of Maunsell in Hong Kong. He was awarded the OBE in 1997 when he was also elected President of the Hong Kong Institution of Engineers.

Sha Tin was the scheme that really ignited the firm's growth in Hong Kong. The social reform implicit in the New Towns programme, the improvement of the living conditions of so many people, appealed to those Maunsell engineers who believed that the best of their work should be directly related to the welfare of the community. Before work on the New Towns began, John Downer remembered sitting with Geoff Fernie in a hotel overlooking the Sha Tin valley. It was an attractive vista of small farms and villages. 'Geoff asked me how I could destroy it all, so I took him down to the resettlement estates and showed him the conditions people were living in.'

As well as Sha Tin, Maunsell worked on four other major New Towns, a commitment which still continued in 2005. One of them, Tseung Kwan O, emerged from a study Maunsell undertook in 1975 into the feasibility of industrial development in the area. In a conclusion that reinforced the firm's professional integrity, Maunsell recommended against any further industrial development because of the adverse impact it would have on the environment. Instead, a few years later, the firm was asked to carry out another study which led to a massive scheme to reclaim and develop land in the area to create a balanced urban development, with a mix of housing, recreational facilities and jobs. Environmental management, a new concept in the early 1970s, was alien to the headlong rush into development being fostered in Hong Kong. Maunsell's ethical approach,

One of the first New Towns developed in Hong Kong in the early 1970s was Sha Tin. Maunsell started work on Sha Tin in 1973 and was still working there in 2005.

The East Kowloon Way and Island Eastern Corridor (shown here) were among several major highways projects carried out by Maunsell in Hong Kong during the 1970s.

apparent in the preparatory and landscaping work done for Sha Tin, was partly responsible for raising environmental awareness in Hong Kong. Environmental management, driven not by professional preference but by the needs of the client and the community, was integral to the renewal of Hong Kong's infrastructure. Early work in this field included a refuse treatment plant and an incinerator.

The expansion of market-led skills was also evident from the firm's highways projects in Hong Kong. By the time Route 4 was completed in 1976, Maunsell was already designing several other expressways. In addition to the Aberdeen Tunnel and its approaches, these included other major urban elevated roadways, such as the East Kowloon Way, the West Kowloon Corridor and the Island Eastern Corridor.

As well as the New Towns and major highways, Maunsell also became involved with work on the fledgling container port at Kwai Chung. Work on this port continues to this day and it has grown to become the largest container port in the world. It was here that the Maunsell tradition of adopting the latest techniques was shown at its best. The port involved reclaiming land from the sea and the normal method was to use material dug out of the nearby hills. Maunsell recognised that this was becoming less cost effective and proposed the use of material dredged from the sea bed. This pioneering method of using marine sand for land reclamation was viewed with scepticism by some but it proved to be brilliantly successful and became the standard technique. Once again Maunsell engineers with the courage of their convictions had been proved right.

This rapid increase in work stretched the firm's resources. More engineers were borrowed from the UK and Australia. Bob Grieve, Craig Mclean, John Clayton and David Odgers came from Australia and Arnold Cameron-Smith, Ron Taylor and Pat Anson from the UK. They all played their part in leading and training the local staff. Local engineers were being recruited in ever increasing

increasing numbers and many of these, such as Patrick Yim, Tony Shum, Michael Lai, Charlton Wong and Dickson Lo, later became directors. Other staff were also sent out to Hong Kong, including highway technicians such as Jim Hocking, draughtsmen such as Harry Howard (one of Maunsell's original team) and quantity surveyors such as Bob Whitehouse.

In meeting the challenges posed by the difficult Hong Kong terrain, particularly the threat of landslides, the firm's engineers became experts in local geology, geotechnical engineering and soil and rock mechanics. This led to the creation of a separate geotechnical services group which became so successful that in 1980 a separate firm, Maunsell Geotechnical Services, was established. Mike Millar was joined by Rob Fraser and Cliff Matson. Apart from working on the geotechnical aspects of the firm's own projects, Geotechnical Services soon found its services in demand in its own right. At the time the Hong Kong government was embarking on a major programme of slope inspection, assessment and strengthening. This provided continuous work and in 2005, under the management of Fred Ng, the firm employed more than 300 staff.

The scope of the firm's work in Hong Kong continued to grow. The firm's first railway project in Hong Kong was the modernisation of the Kowloon-Canton Railway, an essential upgrading of the public transport network. This single track line, the Colony's only railway, was particularly important because it linked four of the planned New Towns – Sha Tin, Tai Po, Fanling and Shek Wu Hui. The upgrading would develop the potential of the line for the mass transportation of passengers but it was also important for the carriage of both passengers and freight to and from mainland China. Maunsell had a major role in designing the new stations along the route.

Then came the Mass Transit Railway (MTR), which would become one of the world's busiest underground railways. Work on the MTR began in 1975 and, like the New Towns, provided continuous work for Maunsell. The firm developed a working arrangement with an American electrical and mechanical engineering firm to offer a complete package of engineering services for several contractors. This relationship eventually led to similar joint projects elsewhere in the world. The two firms worked together on projects such as the motorway network in and around Ankara in Turkey, the Central Expressway in

Maunsell also worked on the container port at Kwai Chung in Hong Kong, the largest such port in the world, introducing the use of sea-dredged land for the reclamation.

Singapore, a sewerage outfall pipe in Taiwan, the Karachi Mass Transit Study in Pakistan and various projects in Australia.

For the first stage of the Hong Kong MTR the firm designed two underground stations and two sections of cut-and-cover tunnels. The client for these was the contractor as the construction had been let on a design and construct basis. This was the first of many such projects as Maunsell's reputation for practical designs and working well with contractors spread quickly. To strengthen the management required for the speedy implementation of these designs, David Hook was sent

Maunsell has worked with the Kowloon-Canton Railway in Hong Kong since 1973. Maunsell continued working with KCRC and designed stations on Westrail.

over for a time from the UK. In fact, throughout this period, Hong Kong relied upon the skills of Maunsell in the UK to execute a stream of major projects while it was developing its own technical capabilities.

In 1977 the firm was appointed firstly to prepare a study for 11 stations on the MTR's Tsuen Wan Extension and then to execute the detailed designs of all the underground stations. Richard Garrett was in charge for the Island Line, the third phase of the MTR begun in 1981, with design assistance from the UK and Australian firms. The Island Line broke new ground in locating underground station concourses in the deep basements of high rise developments. Maunsell led the way in developing new techniques for these designs, where the basements reached a depth of up to thirty metres. Using perimeter diaphragm walls as both a temporary and permanent ground support, the firm developed a method of building the basements from the top down. The buildings above could be built from the bottom up at the same time, thus speeding up the whole process. Once again Maunsell's ideas proved to be practical and economic and the technique has become standard for many of the high-rise buildings in Hong Kong. It was also later used on the Jubilee Line extension of the London Underground.

By this time Maunsell in Hong Kong had established a significant building structural design group. Originally set up by Raymond Ho, the group gradually won more and more high-rise building projects, including several of the developments above the Island Line stations.

In all these areas the firm benefited from the favourable impression it made upon clients and contractors and from its reputation for saving time and money. Although fee competition had appeared in Australia, elsewhere this was still an era when consultancy work was won on merit, when a firm's reputation for meeting the needs of the client was critical. This had always been a crucial part of the Maunsell ethos and was a key factor in the firm's growth in Hong Kong. Shrewd commercial management, inherited from the example shown by Miles Birkett in Australia, allowed Maunsell to balance the needs of the client with professional perfection. Each new project enhanced the firm's reputation for working effectively with contractors. This was demonstrated especially in the Design & Construct contracts which were let for the initial stage of the MTR.

Maunsell was responsible for the Jing Guang Centre in Beijing, China's tallest building at the time.

By the end of the 1970s, the Hong Kong office employed more people and was more profitable than any other part of the international Maunsell organisation. But it was not a case of uninterrupted success. Francis Bong will never forget his involvement with the major redundancies that took place in Hong Kong in the early 1980s following a downturn in the Hong Kong economy. The recession proved short-lived and economic growth in the Colony resumed in the mid-1980s.

While Maunsell in Hong Kong continued to rely largely on the local economy, the huge potential of the Chinese market was obvious. After the death of Mao in 1976, the iron curtain was drawn back and foreign tourists were admitted in 1979. As the Chinese government welcomed foreign aid, Maunsell took part in several infrastructure projects through the Australian firm. In Hong Kong, Francis Bong was given a watching brief for China where the firm maintained its limited presence throughout the 1980s. This helped Maunsell to find its feet in a new market, to learn how and with whom to do business. Once again the importance of creating long-lasting relationships would have long-term benefits for the firm.

The Building Engineering Group (BEG), Maunsell's structural engineering group in Hong Kong, was responsible for one of the key Chinese projects undertaken during the 1980s. Beijing's

209 metre high Jing Guang Centre was China's tallest building at the time. This was just one example of the sort of building for which Maunsell in Hong Kong won a growing reputation. The Group had begun by identifying an opportunity for major buildings arising from Hong Kong's prosperity and the increasing affluence of its population and businesses. Another significant Chinese project was the Waihai Bridge. Built over an arm of the Pearl river, it was nearly 2.5 kilometres long. The central section used balanced cantilever arms with matchcast segments, which in true Maunsell fashion was based on the Australian Bowen Bridge. It was a worthy successor to the Hammersmith Flyover.

In 1988 John Downer stood down as chief executive of MCA, handing over to Francis Bong, but remained as chairman. During his time, MCA had been transformed from a three-man operation to the largest engineering consultancy in Asia outside Japan, employing 765 staff with associate offices in Kuala Lumpur, Bangkok and Singapore and representatives in Beijing and Tokyo. The first three were rapidly expanding cities in countries whose economies enjoyed remarkable growth during the 1970s and 1980s. With economic growth came foreign aid and investment poured into infrastructure projects. With a reputation for innovation and flexibility, Maunsell was ideally placed to take advantage of this. So, for example, work on the shipyards in Singapore was followed by the Benjamin Shears Bridge, a design and construct contract won on the basis of the flyover design. It was the first Maunsell structure to appear on a banknote. Other notable projects included the Singapore Convention & Exhibition Centre, which incorporated a space frame roof, and in Indonesia the port of Tanjung Priok.

The Benjamin Shears Bridge in Singapore was completed in 1982.

10

The Revival of Maunsell in Australia

Hong Kong, in John Laurie's words, became 'an absolute powerhouse' for the international firm. For Maunsell in the UK and Australia, where the flow of work was becoming susceptible to the ebb and flow of the national economies, work from Hong Kong was vital. This work was especially invaluable in the early 1970s for Maunsell in Australia, which was recovering from the trauma of the West Gate Bridge. As a result, the Australian firm won an Australian Export Award as early as 1972.

It took time to rebuild morale and develop new areas of business in Australia. The reputation Maunsell had established during the 1960s stood it in good stead. John Laurie, who was managing the firm's Sydney office in 1970, recalled how one client rang him the day after the Royal Commission reported on the West Gate Bridge disaster and said 'I think you need a job'. Laurie urged staff to put the event behind them and concentrate on rebuilding the business. It appeared at first as if the economic climate would help Maunsell achieve this. Gough Whitlam's 1972 Labor government embarked at breakneck speed on an extensive spending programme. It hoped to emulate in other parts of Australia the achievements of the NCDC in Canberra. One of the new towns intended to meet the country's growing population was Albury and in anticipation Maunsell opened a small office there under David Odgers in 1974. By then, however, the Australian economy was beginning to suffer indirectly from the international world oil crisis. Trade collapsed, unemployment rose, inflation soared, Whitlam's government was dismissed, the Australian new towns programme was abandoned and government expenditure on major public works was cut back.

Things were made more difficult because of fee competition between firms. John Laurie, who would later become President of the ACEA, was chairman of the sub-committee responsible for fee scales during the period when they were being outlawed by the Australian government in response to pressure from federal and State client organisations. This happened at a time when inflation was rising, fees were being cut and margins were disappearing. So firms went out of business as a cycle of falling fees brought less satisfactory designs, increasing client dissatisfaction and therefore producing less work. Compared with other firms, Maunsell coped well with this change, thanks to an established reputation for high standards forged by Miles Birkett. But the issue dogged the profession in Australia just at the time when Maunsell could have done without it.

Both Laurie and Jim Leslie knew that the firm could not rely indefinitely on work from Hong Kong. Maunsell & Partners would succeed or fail based on its performance in Australia. They realised they had to take over the high profile marketing role previously undertaken single-handedly by Miles Birkett – 'we had to grow up very quickly'. Just as the UK firm was known principally for its work on motorways, so the reputation of the Australian firm was still based largely on the major bridges it had designed. This era was coming to an end as economic recession hit the country – the last significant example was the elegant award-winning Stirling Bridge in Fremantle, completed in 1974. It was time to diversify.

Maunsell took advantage of the rapid development of Australia's energy and minerals sectors on which the country relied for most of its foreign earnings. In 1970, through Geoff Fernie and the Perth office, the firm had been appointed to carry out an Environmental Impact Study for an aluminium manufacturing project in Western Australia. This opened up the environmental services sector for Maunsell and the firm won several similar commissions for the Western Mining Corporation in Western Australia from 1976. Further work ranged from a study into the effects of uranium mining at Yeelirrie to wave investigation supported by computer modelling for Port Hedland Harbour. For an international consortium of oil companies, Maunsell made an assessment of the environmental impact of the proposed North West Shelf LNG project. This, in turn, led to work on the design and construction of the 1,550 kilometre long Dampier-Perth LNG pipeline. The project management, design, supervision and monitoring of the project was carried out with Fluor Australia, the subsidiary of a US firm. This was another example of a joint

Port Botany, completed during the 1970s, with most of the key elements designed by Maunsell, is Sydney's major maritime container terminal.

working arrangement whose advantages for the client lay in the combination of skills offered by the respective partners. This huge scheme, worth A$925 million, ran from 1978 to 1996, bringing certainty to the firm's finances, although, as John Laurie confessed, the firm 'grappled with profits from time to time', tending to think more in terms of the development of staff rather than profitability. But it was this ethos that in part attracted people to the firm. Mike Worrall, for instance, joined the firm in Melbourne in 1975, left in 1976 but came back in 1977 – 'the people brought me back'.

The firm's strength in transport planning developed from its work in Canberra, which continued until the late 1980s. This was enhanced by the creation of a specific transport planning group in 1973 under the direction of Tony Herbert. He had joined the firm in 1964 and was one of those chosen by Miles Birkett to run the Canberra office. The firm also had the advantage of handling design work for Hong Kong. A major breakthrough came in the mid-1980s when the firm adopted and adapted an advanced computer software program, MOSS (Modelling Of Surface Systems), already well-known in the industry.

Throughout the firm there has always been a long and continuing tradition of collaboration on the development and application of computer technology within the firm, largely under the direction of Roger Wright in the UK, Tony Herbert in Australia and Malcolm Pearson in Hong Kong. The three men attended Maunsell's first international computer meeting in Australia in 1983 with the aim of assisting strategic planning. This meeting led directly to the creation of the Maunsell Systems Centre in Melbourne in 1985 under the direction of Tony Herbert. In the following year a Technical Systems Committee was established following a meeting in London and lasted for several years. By the end of the 1980s there was a Systems Centre in the UK and Hong Kong as well as Australia. With advancing technology, data could be transferred from one to another, creating an international network. At the same time the Group began to capitalise on advances in personal computers in the late 1980s and early 1990s.

The revision of MOSS was pioneered by the Systems Centre and it revolutionised the speed and accuracy of design work and calculations, transforming draughtsmen into knowledgeable, highly skilled and much sought after designers. Throughout the Maunsell organisation the evolving role of draughtsmen and other support staff over many years has been one on which the firm has depended.

As well as applying modern technology to transport planning, the firm also pioneered the application of microcomputer technology to building design. This helped Maunsell in Australia to gain a reputation for the design of major buildings. One award-winning example was the National Tennis Centre at Melbourne Park, with its retractable roof, completed in 1989, which hosts the Australian Open Tennis Championship each year. A merger of the Perth office with the Perth structural engineering consultancy of Halpern Glick in the same year strengthened the

The National Tennis Centre in Melbourne, with its retractable roof, completed in 1989, was a prize-winning example of a design generated by Maunsell through the application of pioneering micro-computer technology. It is a great example of Maunsell's ability to handle unusual structures.

firm's presence in this new sector. Halpern Glick, founded by Leon Halpern in 1947, had been responsible for many commercial and civic buildings as well as infrastructure projects. The merger was a reflection of the trend towards the consolidation of the profession into larger firms. Halpern Glick Maunsell, as it became known, was a success, largely because of the common culture and ethical approach shared by both firms.

Another Maunsell innovation in Australia was the Tremie Tube. Although it was only of minor significance for the firm, it demonstrated an intellectual curiosity that lay behind so many of the worldwide firm's engineering advances. Aimed at Australia's huge grain industry, the Tremie Tube was designed to reduce the pressure on the walls of concrete silos during the discharge of grain, thus saving millions of dollars in maintenance and replacement costs. It gained yet another ACEA engineering award for Maunsell in 1985.

The firm's skills in bridge construction were once again demonstrated in 1982 on the Bowen Bridge, close to the Tasman Bridge completed nearly 20 years earlier. The foundations of the Bowen Bridge were most unusual, comprising massive gravity caissons, up to 40 metres deep, built inside precast cofferdams 14 metres in diameter. The huge mass of concrete was required to resist a head-on collision from vessels of up to 5,000 tonnes, essential after the damage caused to the Tasman Bridge.

Expertise in urban development and transport planning helped Maunsell to become the first international consulting engineering to win work in China. Through its presence in countries from Malaysia to Turkey, the Australian firm had shown itself to be equally as internationalist in outlook as the other parts of the firm. Thanks to Maunsell's international activities, the firm's Australian engineers were reckoned to have worked in some 45 countries. Maunsell was appointed to undertake the Shanghai Urban Study, which was part-funded by the Australian government. Four years later, the firm also won the contract to review the designs of the proposed Beijing-Tianjing expressway in China, financed by the Australian government in association with the World Bank. Maunsell showed its awareness of local cultures and the importance it placed on client relationships by submitting its proposals, under a red cover with gold lettering, shortly before the Chinese New Year, hugely impressing the Chinese.

By this time, Maunsell in Australia, under John Laurie as chairman and Jim Leslie as managing director, employed nearly 300 staff. With head office in Melbourne, the firm had six regional offices plus four associated offices, serving every State capital in the country. The transfer of expertise that had served Maunsell so well overseas also had benefits within Australia where each office, although working with a fair degree of independence, lent its skills to others, with technical support from head office in Melbourne.

Maunsell in the UK

While the 1970s saw the growth of the firm in Hong Kong and the revival of the firm in Australia, for Maunsell in the UK it was a decade that saw a repeat of the pattern of the firm's early years - a decline in work at home compensated by new work from overseas. Throughout this period the UK firm operated in a difficult home market and was repeatedly called upon to send its best engineers to support the worldwide group, notably in Hong Kong, yet it continued to execute major projects in the UK.

In 1970, when the firm moved out of central London to new head offices in nearby Penge, the Labour government was replaced by Edward Heath's Conservatives. The new government was equally committed to spending on public works. So the first few years of the new decade saw the firm working on the completion of the Westway, the first stretch of the M53 motorway that was intended to link Liverpool with north Wales but never quite made it, and the M63 motorway north of Manchester as well as a variety of city ring roads and trunk roads. In addition, after the collapse of the Milford Haven and West Gate Bridges, the firm was also given the job of checking most of the steel girder bridges throughout the UK. This, together with the regional highways work carried out by the firm, led to the opening of two offices, one in Birmingham, the other in Manchester.

But most of these projects were coming to an end as the fortunes of the British economy deteriorated. By the end of 1973, the country was in the grip of soaring inflation, rising unemployment and frequent, crippling strikes. Matters were made worse by the huge rise in international oil prices that followed. The growth rate for the British economy halved as another Labour government struggled to curb inflationary wage increases and mounting job losses. Government cutbacks in highways spending announced in the summer of 1973 were just a foretaste of worse to come. The construction and building industries were badly affected. Once again, as the notes for the London office recorded in The Maunsell Whisper at the end of 1973, the firm was aware that 'one of our problems in London is that we need to export to survive'.

Another problem in the UK was a disregard for profitability even greater than in Australia. In fact, the Australian firm had been asked to send their accountant to London in 1971 to investigate the state of the UK firm's finances. He concluded that that poor financial management, excessive

The M25 was a leading example of the many highways projects carried out by Maunsell in the UK.

research and development, and a whimsical approach to fee levels and job costings were responsible for a consistently poor financial record, masked by occasional freak profits and by the surplus from Westway. The firm had not been helped by its professional disdain for marketing in order to win work. This apparent disregard for profits stemmed from the pursuit of work which interested the firm rather than work which would have created a sustainable business in the UK. But this was in the tradition of Guy Maunsell himself. While the firm retained the ability to seek out and secure projects throughout the world, which depended upon the firm's technical excellence, its business results reflected the financial volatility of those projects.

Because of this, the UK firm was desperate for design work from Hong Kong to keep it going. Other attempts to win overseas work had been mixed. Among the successes were the Temerloh Bridge over the Sungei Pahang in Malaysia, completed in 1975, the elevated East Coast Parkway in Singapore and the invitation from the Egyptian government to lead a study into the deepening and widening of the Suez Canal.

But the rise in oil prices, which crippled many Western economies, also created unprecedented prosperity in the oil producing states of the Middle East. With a dearth of work at home and the prospect of riches abroad, there was intense competition among British consulting engineers for work in the Middle East. Nevertheless, it was an opportunity Maunsell in the UK could not afford to ignore.

David Lee, whose father had been a British official in Iran, knew something of the Middle East but the firm was also fortunate to possess a native Arabic speaker among its British staff. In late 1974 Shakir Al-Kubaisi, who had joined the firm in 1969, was sent to explore opportunities in Iraq, his home country. He opened an office in Baghdad in 1975 and very quickly the firm acquired the commission to design the Adhamiyah Bridge, the first cable-stayed bridge in the Middle East. Other valuable bridge and highway projects followed but the most important was the Baghdad International Airport in 1979. It was a huge scheme that utilised more than 200 engineers, architects, draughtsmen and other technical staff. Many staff found themselves undertaking work they had never done before. Kubaisi himself designed the lighting layout for the runway. The firm completed the design and tender documents within two weeks of the six month deadline. It transformed the UK firm, which learned from the Baghdad airport the commercial lessons already learned by the firm in Hong Kong – the importance of adhering to deadlines and budgets and striking the right balance between research and development and the needs of the client. What

is truly remarkable about the Baghdad airport project is that the UK business had little or no previous airport experience and yet it had the confidence in its own technical capability to take on such a major undertaking as almost its first venture in this sector. Maunsell also carried out a similar role in Iraq for Basra International Airport.

Maunsell designed the first cable-stayed bridge built in the Middle East, the Adhamiyah Bridge over the River Tigris in Baghdad.

Coincidentally, Maunsell also acted subsequently as a contractual adviser for the French contractor appointed to construct the Baghdad airport. The firm with its sub consultants, checked more than 25,000 working drawings prepared by the contractor. This work came about through the UK firm's French subsidiary based in Paris. This had been formed in 1979 after the firm's collaboration with a French company working on a project to construct an oil platform for the North Sea. Maunsell recognised the opportunity to offer contractual services to French companies working outside France on English language contracts. It was another pioneering venture in which

Baghdad International Airport was completed in 1983. Maunsell in the UK was the lead consultant for the Tender Design and Documentation.

the firm was breaking new ground. Once the French office was opened, the firm built up similar relationships with several other major French construction companies. For example, Maunsell would work with one contractor, GTM, on several major projects over the years, including the Channel Crossing study and the Second Severn Crossing in the UK. This was just one example of the importance of building up long-term relationships that David Lee was always encouraging.

The firm's success in Iraq came to an end with the advent of the Iran-Iraq war in 1980. By now, John Baxter had retired as managing partner, handing over in 1978 to David Lee. Competition between consulting engineers on fees was just beginning to affect the UK profession, which was having to become more commercial, and this was one of the reasons why G Maunsell & Partners began to operate as a limited liability company from 1984. David Lee became chairman and David Hook was appointed managing director. Lee was an effective ambassador for the firm, constantly making new contacts, which often brought dividends through new work in future years. He believed in the importance of personal contact, not just with clients but also with staff, a view shared by many of those directing Maunsell across the world during this period. He was perfectly complemented by David Hook, a modest, quiet, generous man, who dealt with the details of day-to-day business that Lee often found difficult to come to grips with. The change from a partnership to a corporate organisation was not an easy one for the firm. For several years, the new company was still run as a partnership. In the belief that the well-qualified professional civil engineer could turn his hand to anything, the firm promoted good engineers to positions usually occupied by professional non-engineering executives. Diverted from their real expertise, those who made the transition with success were rare.

With the effective end of the firm's work in the Middle East – although Maunsell completed a number of projects in Oman, including a 747 Jumbo Jet hangar and a major mountainous highway – and the onset of another recession in the UK, David Lee and David Hook were faced with considerable challenges by the early 1980s. In fact, the response of the firm encompassed the expansion

The 78 kilometre Mughsayl to Furious Road in a rugged region of southern Oman, dominated by a mountain range rising to 1,000 metres, was designed by Maunsell who also supervised the construction. It took three years to build and was completed in 1985.

of its activities at home and abroad, the enhancement of its reputation in new and existing areas of design, and the acquisition of additional skills.

In the UK the new Conservative government of Margaret Thatcher was intent on shaking the British economy out of its state of torpor. The way in which this was done was a mixed blessing for firms like Maunsell that relied so heavily on publicly funded projects. The recession of the early 1980s was the most severe to affect Britain since the 1930s. Government spending was curtailed and many proposed

In the 1980s Maunsell in the UK was involved in work on London's new major orbital motorway, the M25.

schemes either abandoned or curtailed. It was obvious that Maunsell's workload in the UK would eventually peter out unless replacement projects were found.

But Margaret Thatcher was also the apostle of privatisation, transferring to the private sector activities that had long been the preserve of government. So Maunsell benefited from one of the Thatcher government's first privatisations. The Regional Construction Units (RCU) of the Department of Transport had been established in the 1960s, principally for the design and construction of the UK's expanding motorway network. The RCUs often ran sub-units located within their region. In 1981 the government decided to privatise the RCUs and their sub-units. For Maunsell, it was an obvious opportunity to expand the firm's UK activities at a time when business was becoming difficult. Maunsell was interested in a sub-unit based at Witham in Essex. Among the schemes currently managed by the sub-unit were a major section of the new London orbital motorway, the M25, and bypasses at three major East Anglian towns, Chelmsford, Colchester and Ipswich. Unusually, the choice of consultant to take over each unit was in the hands of the RCU staff. At Witham the staff viewed several consultants. They chose Maunsell. While the firm brought several clear advantages, including a non-contributory pension scheme and a promise to retain the office and staff, what particularly impressed the Witham staff was the quality of Maunsell's staff and partners, notably David Hook. As a result, the Witham sub-unit became part of Maunsell in October 1981.

It was the first acquisition ever made by the UK firm, increasing the firm's staff from around 250 to 360. During the rest of the 1980s the Witham office concentrated on a series of major road schemes, notably the upgrading of the North Circular London orbital road and the Norwich southern bypass. There were attempts at diversification through the private sector but few of these bore fruit. There were many reasons for this. The firm in the UK was not able to take the financial risks required by the private sector, instead reinvesting its scarce resources on research and development, although ultimately much of this proved to be unfruitful commercially.

The innovative Second Severn Crossing, completed in 1996, revitalised Maunsell's business in the UK.

Maunsell's main sphere of work in the UK continued to be in highways and transportation. While the growth in traffic stimulated plans for new road schemes, it also increased the pressure on the existing network. Maunsell won more and more maintenance work, which became an important sector of the market. A typical example occurred in 1979 when the firm was commissioned to inspect all the concrete road viaducts in the Midlands. Almost a decade later, Maunsell took part in a joint project with another consulting engineering firm for the maintenance of the M5 and M6 motorways around Birmingham.

The work on the Norwich southern bypass led to the opening of another regional office in Norwich in 1983. This was part of a pattern that saw several further regional offices, such as Newcastle and Bristol, opened during the 1980s as clients wanted to employ consultants located more closely to the projects with which they were involved.

The Witham office assisted the London office on the designs for other Maunsell projects at home and abroad, notably the study for the Second Severn Crossing (SSC) and the Hong Kong MTR. The SSC was a project that significantly enhanced Maunsell's reputation in the UK. It was one of several important steel bridges on which the firm worked during the 1980s. The firm's first major cable-stayed steel bridge had been the Batman Bridge in Australia but it was Maunsell's design for the Adhamiyah Bridge in Iraq, which stimulated the flurry of work on steel bridges during the 1980s.

In 1984 Maunsell was jointly commissioned to carry out a study of the alternatives for a new crossing over the river Severn. Maunsell's team was led by David Lee and Dr Brian Richmond, who had left academic work to join the firm in 1968 and had worked on the West Gate Bridge. After completing the study, the joint venture partners succeeded in winning the appointment to prepare the tender design and Maunsell alone was then invited to act as agent for the government during the construction. The design, in the best traditions of Guy Maunsell, was not only aesthetically pleasing; it was also supremely practical, incorporating such features as replaceable steel tendons, windshields to minimise closure due to high winds, and easy inspection. As with previous ventures worldwide, the project also provided great opportunities for a new generation of young engineers within the firm and eventually led to Maunsell's involvement with other major new bridges, such as the Stonecutter's Bridge in Hong Kong and the Rion-Antirion Bridge over the Gulf of Corinth in Greece.

Among more recent projects in which Maunsell has been involved is the Stonecutter's Bridge, spanning the Rambler Channel in Hong Kong. Work started in 2004 and the bridge is expected to be completed in 2008.

The Rion-Antirion Bridge is a 2,250 metre long cable-stayed bridge linked the Peloponnese to the Greek mainland. This bridge was built, in a seismic area where foundations were difficult and the depth of the water reached 60 metres, at a cost of EUR 800.000.000. Maunsell was appointed as the Independent Supervision Engineer for the contract for both the Concessionaire and the Greek Government.

The SSC was a pioneering project in many ways. It lasted from 1984 until the five kilometre long bridge was opened in 1996 and revitalised the firm in the UK. Although many of Maunsell's big bridges around the world had been seen as catalysts for economic and social activity, these considerations became for the first time a central part of the justification for the SSC. But in addition to measuring the potential social and economic benefits of the SSC, the 1984 study also took into account the environmental impact of a major new structure in such a sensitive location. The bridge was built between 1992 and 1996 under an innovative private finance contract and completed within budget and timescale and without controversy.

Among the team of talented engineers who worked on the SSC was Peter Head, who had joined the firm from Freeman Fox in 1980, attracted by what he later called 'the seamless approach between contractor and consultant'. He assumed increasingly responsibility for the project and was awarded the OBE (Officer of the Order of the British Empire) for his contribution. Head had a passion for bridges that other engineers rarely expressed, remarking some years later that 'there's something almost spiritual about a bridge that is difficult to define. It's not just that they connect people and communities, but they somehow engage the imagination'.

He was also behind another of the innovations pioneered by the firm during the 1980s. In 1981 the firm was asked to investigate how maintenance access could be improved to a viaduct carrying a major trunk road, the A19, over the river Tees in the north of England. Head believed that enclosing the bridge in a rigid plastic box in the form of an access deck would not only fulfil the requirements for access but also help to retard corrosion. He looked at the reinforced plastic being used in naval minesweepers and this began a protracted decade-long period of research and development into what became known as ACCS (Advanced Composite Construction System). The patented material was used to enclose the Tees viaduct in 1988 but neither Maunsell nor the industry embraced ACCS with much enthusiasm as a construction material. While ACCS won several awards, it was much less widely used than anticipated - there was a small footbridge in the UK, at Aberfeldy in Scotland in 1992; the 'Caretaker' bridge enclosure system; small prefabricated and modular buildings; and other minor applications. It is now being made under licence in the USA and is used in modest quantities around the world.

While the UK firm's already considerable reputation for bridge design was enhanced by the SSC, Maunsell's international reputation for mass transit systems provided a boost to the UK firm in an area where it had limited experience. By the early 1980s London's old-established docks had fallen into disuse as ports further downstream and on the coast were developed to handle the much larger ships built to carry containers. The government was keen to regenerate the area and the London Docklands Development Corporation was formed in 1982. One of the key tasks of the new Corporation was to create the transport infrastructure to attract and support new businesses. It was imperative that any new transport system was relatively inexpensive and could be completed quickly. The result was the Docklands Light Railway (DLR). The initial section was begun in 1984 and finished only three years later. Using existing or abandoned railway alignments wherever possible, the DLR was the UK's first automated light rail transit system. Maunsell was appointed to carry out the preliminary civil design study and also undertook the final design in association with the successful contractors. Peter Gray, who had returned to the UK from Hong Kong, was among the Maunsell party that made a presentation to members of London Transport, joint partners in the venture with the Docklands Corporation. He recalled that the simple fact he mentioned he had been in Hong Kong was sufficient to impress them even though he himself had had no involvement with the Hong Kong Mass Transit Railway.

Even before the initial section of the railway was opened, Maunsell designed for a contractor an extension of the DLR to London's existing Bank underground railway station. The contract was awarded in July 1987 and completed four years later. A key part of the design was a 1.6 kilometre long tunnel, which relied on Maunsell's extensive work on railway tunnels in Hong Kong. Maunsell's contribution to this major project subsequently helped the firm to win other major commissions, notably the London Underground Jubilee Line extension and the Copenhagen Metro, both in the 1990s.

Maunsell's work on the DLR led to one significant engineering innovation related to tunnelling. This was a software program that transformed the process known as wriggling, that is, matching the alignment of the track to the shape of the tunnels and the kinematic envelope of the trains to ensure proper clearances. Previously achieved by diagrams, Maunsell's Wriggle program revolutionized the process, saving time and money. It is still used within the industry.

Another addition to the skills of the UK firm came through the acquisition of D Balfour & Sons in 1989. Balfour was an old-established business, founded in 1882, with a particular strength in environmental engineering and a presence in many overseas countries as well as the UK. With Balfour came Consultants in Environmental Sciences (CES), which Balfour had formed in 1982 to develop work in scientific consultancy and research and

During the 1980s Maunsell was heavily involved in design work for various phases of the Docklands Light Railway in London, including the initial phase and the subsequent extension to the existing Bank underground railway station.

development, concentrated especially on water and wastewater science and technology. CES also had a reputation for industrial waste management and dealing with contaminated land. Through Balfour's overseas links, CES forged a particularly strong presence in Asia, based in Hong Kong.

By the late 1980s, Maunsell in the UK had established a reputation for major projects based on serving the worldwide group with technical expertise. The UK firm had benefited from this process by embracing, after several abortive attempts, new skills, thanks in particular to the expertise of the Hong Kong firm. As well as its traditional highways work, the UK firm was now involved in several major rail projects and, through Balfour and CES, was making an important contribution in the environmental field overseas. But although Maunsell in the UK now employed more than 700 staff and was winning projects demanding large design teams, it was still under-represented within its home market, both in terms of the geographic distribution of its offices and the skills and services it brought to that market.

The Copenhagen Metro was one of several commissions won by Maunsell following its success with the Docklands Light Railway.

Part 4
1989-1999

12

Forging a Group Identity

New skills provided greater opportunities for more staff and progress towards the all-round service clients were coming to expect from consulting engineers. But Maunsell's problem around the world was that it could only afford to add this expertise by acquisition if the company being acquired was relatively small. There was just not enough capital for the firm to invest in new skills. Yet the example of Halpern Glick in Australia had already demonstrated that the future for the profession lay in increasing the scope and scale of individual firms. This was a conundrum that would tax Maunsell for the next ten years.

The worldwide nature of the firm, combined with the skills it could offer, at least provided the opportunity to enter projects jointly with other international partners to offer a comprehensive range of services. But joint projects only highlighted the firm's deficiency in certain areas. They also masked the lack of coherence at international level. Regional and local priorities prevailed, although each of the three firms was more than happy to exchange staff and provide technical support for each other. The UK firm in particular, having been impatient during the early 1970s with the lack of financial progress made by the Hong Kong business, now found it hard to adjust to Hong Kong's increasing importance within Maunsell; the Hong Kong firm, on the other hand, resented the fact that its growth did not bring it the influence it felt it deserved within the international group.

By the mid-1980s the existing corporate structure was no longer adequate for an international group with obvious potential for further expansion. As part of a strategy review, David Hook drew up a paper in the autumn of 1986 in which he outlined how the firm was perceived internationally as a familiar name with an ill-defined nature. He discovered that Maunsell's image was much clearer in the UK, Australia and Hong Kong, the firm's three principal operating areas. He pointed out that 'to succeed internationally we need a strong unified image of a powerful group of firms with a common style'. This was especially important if associate firms were to feel a full part of the Group. He suggested that any worldwide corporate structure should ensure that 'international interests are not subordinated to local interest'.

The answer, which emerged in 1989, was the creation of Guy Maunsell International Ltd (GMIL) as an international holding company, under John Downer as chief executive. The corporate goals laid out for GMIL embraced all the characteristics with which Maunsell had been imbued by its founder and that each succeeding generation, whether in the UK or overseas, had perpetuated – good client relationships, practical designs, the recognition of contractors as allies, technical leadership and innovation, good communications, a good working environment, contributing to the well-being of the community and a respect for the natural environment. With a Chief Executives' Committee, consisting of the chief executives of each of the regions, UK, Australia, Hong Kong, the Middle East and South East Asia, meeting regularly to discuss international strategy, this was intended to bring together the operations of all the firms 'into a planned and motivated group'.

GMIL was owned jointly by Maunsell Holdings Pty (Australia), G Maunsell & Partners International Ltd (UK) and Maunsell Hong Kong Ltd. Although the Hong Kong firm now held 20 per cent of the international business, this ratio scarcely did justice to Hong Kong's success and its financial contribution to the rest of the Maunsell Group. The new structure also preserved the holding company's cross-holding of 20 per cent in each of the individual firms. The predominant shareholding of the two older firms was an historical anomaly that proved difficult to resolve to the satisfaction of all the shareholders.

Overcoming this problem was also tied up with what became known as consolidation. This was a word repeated frequently in the minutes of the international board for over a decade. The idea behind consolidation was the creation of an international company that owned 100 per cent of the regional businesses. Many felt strongly that this would help to develop Maunsell as a group, produce an international business that could respond more rapidly to market forces and allow Maunsell to build up capital to fund growth by acquisition. While the latter point would become more and more important over the years, each objective was inextricably linked with the other as far as the future of the business was concerned.

It quickly became apparent that the Group Chief Executive had very little authority over the regional chief executives. He was forced to rely solely on his powers of persuasion but these were often insufficient to win over board representatives from one or other of the shareholding companies. The latter were usually too consumed with the day-to-day management of their own affairs to have much time for the Group's international development. As a result, the Group was more a collection of separate regional businesses, which had little unity of purpose and over whose direction the Group leadership had little influence. This mattered less when the businesses were performing well than when they were performing badly. The difficulties were apparent to everyone. In 1992 the GMIL board agreed that 'the present situation contained the seeds of the Group's disintegration'. John Downer was passionate in his belief that 'our subordinates aspire to enjoy this firm as we have, and we have a duty to hand it over to them in the best possible shape'.

Thanks to Downer stamping his authority on the process, the interminable discussions on consolidation eventually resulted in GMIL taking a stake of 65 per cent in each of the regional businesses. This stopped fragmentation but did not prevent continued aggravation, essentially over share values. In any given year the results from either Australia or the UK varied while those from Hong Kong were consistently strong. There was also a difference of opinion over the effect a stronger Group would have on local decision making. Those who supported consolidation felt that 'enterprising development' would not be stifled and that 'the traditions and strengths of local management are being preserved through the regional executive system'.

Yet this long-lasting debate should not obscure the fact that, as the Group Chief Executive pointed out in 1992, 'our successful operation and our professional reputation in three continents of the world are the envy of many consultants'. By 1990 the Group as a whole had a turnover of some US$120m, more than 2,000 staff and was among the top 25 international engineering design firms. Whatever the issues that divided those directing the business, they still had much more in common, bound together by a commitment to Guy Maunsell's founding principles. As John Downer noted in 1998, 'the egalitarian principles set out by Guy Maunsell have generated harmony and teamwork and have created a firm that is admired by our peers'. Although there was healthy competition between all parts of the Group, there was also a commitment to supporting each other when help was needed. Regional independence was matched by an international interdependence.

Diversification & Acquisition in Australia

For Maunsell in Australia, the early 1990s were tough. The firm had been appointed project engineer for the proposed Northshore Noosa tourist complex on Queensland's Sunshine Coast. This was a very sensitive environment and the firm's involvement seemed to run counter to the principles it espoused. The proposal created such an outcry that it was eventually abandoned but not before Maunsell, whose contract was based on an equity stake in the venture linked to future profits, had incurred substantial costs. The losses made by the firm more than outweighed the profits it made in an exceptional year. Matters were not helped by the deterioration of the Australian economy, with a rising national debt, widening trade deficit, increasing unemployment and interest rates, which hit almost 20 per cent at their peak. The firm, under a new chief executive, David Odgers, who took over in 1989, had no choice but to retrench and rebuild, leaning heavily on support from the UK and Hong Kong.

While this process was going on, both John Laurie and Jim Leslie retired. Leslie retired as managing director in 1992 and Laurie as chairman in the following year, both after nearly 35 years with Maunsell. Laurie's services to engineering were recognised in 2003 when he was awarded the AC (Companion of the Order of Australia).

In 1994, despite a more competitive market place, Maunsell once again made a profit in Australia. The firm's recovery and subsequent growth during the 1990s was based on the expansion of its skills through diversification and acquisition. There were three key areas. The first was highways and transportation. A decade after the process had occurred in the UK, the Australian government scaled down the volume of planning and design work carried out by the transport agencies of the State governments. In 1992 this encouraged Maunsell to acquire Denis Johnston & Associates, a leading transport planning and traffic engineering consultant. This was

Sydney's Eastern Distributor Tollway is one of many such projects completed by Maunsell Australia.

the same year as the opening of Sydney's M5 Tollway, designed by Maunsell. As the government began to reinvest in the country's inadequate transport infrastructure, Maunsell dominated the tollway sector, working on similar projects in Sydney, Adelaide, Brisbane and Perth. In a joint venture partnership, Maunsell also carried out studies on the upgrading of the railfreight corridors between Brisbane, Sydney and Melbourne.

The second key area was mining. Although the firm had provided ancillary services to the mining industry, it had never been directly involved in projects connected with Australia's most important industry. In October 1998 Maunsell merged with the Queensland firm of McIntyre & Associates, formed in 1951, and its mining subsidiary, MAMIC. The merger was concluded by David Odgers, who left shortly afterwards to take over from John Downer as Group Chief Executive, and Nigel Robinson, Odgers's successor in Australia. This led to work for Western Mining Corporation at the huge Olympic Dam uranium and copper mine and for the Ridgeway and Telfer gold mines. The McIntyre merger helped Maunsell become the third largest mining and minerals consulting engineer in Australia. With the addition of 250 staff from McIntyre, the number of Maunsell's employees had increased from some 120 in 1989 to 700 in 1998.

The third area was work overseas. The firm continued to work on mainly aid-related projects. The most notable example of such a project during the 1990s was the $100m My Thuan Bridge in Vietnam. Designed in Sydney, the 350m long structure was the first cable-stayed bridge in the country as well as the first crossing over the Mekong delta. Nigel Robinson attended the official opening, complete with military honours, in 2000. With more than a million Vietnamese taking the opportunity to cross the Bridge, spontaneous applause broke out to greet the official party of which Robinson was a member. It was, he recalled, an amazing experience.

The My Thuan Bridge, designed by Maunsell in Australia and opened in 2000, was Vietnam's first cable-stayed bridge and the first crossing over the Mekong delta.

Gradually the firm established a presence in several South East Asian countries. In 1995 the Australian firm was operating in both Malaysia, through an associate firm, Maunsell Sharma Zakaria, and in the Philippines. This presence survived the collapse of the region's economy in 1997-8. It was part of an international strategy implemented by the Group in 1994 when five regional zones were created around the world – UK/Europe, the Middle East, Hong Kong/China, South East Asia and Australia/Indonesia – in a conscious effort to develop the potential of these markets. When the collapse of the South East Asian economy made this arrangement untenable, the whole of the region came under the umbrella of the Australian firm. By 1999, the firm had recovered from the costly mistakes of a decade earlier and had also grown significantly at home and overseas, making considerable strides at the same time towards creating a more effective form of corporate management.

The Friendship Bridge, completed in 1994, linking Laos with Thailand over the Mekong, was one example of the aid-related projects carried out by Maunsell Australia.

Suntec City in Singapore, a complex of commercial buildings and a large convention centre with space frame roof.

Maunsell in the UK

In the UK, Maunsell concentrated on the home market during the early 1990s. It had never really made the most of the opportunities available in Europe even though it had a long-established French subsidiary and in 1994 formed a jointly owned company with the Dutch firm, Grontmij, with offices in Holland, Belgium and Germany, focusing on environmental engineering. Attempts to exploit the Eastern European market after the collapse of communism in the late 1980s and early 1990s were largely abortive. Despite the creation of the UK/Europe regional zone in 1994, it was not until the late 1990s that a concerted effort was made to capture work in Eastern Europe, notably in Poland. Greater success was achieved through an alliance with Roughan & O'Donovan in Dublin in the 1990s, which created one of the top three highways engineering consultancies in the Republic of Ireland.

The UK market itself was extremely difficult. As well as the recession that afflicted the UK economy, privatisation was eroding the firm's traditional markets and fee competition was squeezing profits. So, although the firm remained busy, the level of work varied enormously, margins were poor and the firm suffered financially. Nevertheless, despite this background, the firm still secured and carried out several major projects.

One of these was the contract to design and supervise the construction of the Green Park to Waterloo section of the extension to London Underground's Jubilee Line. The DLR had been so successful that, combined with the further development of Canary Wharf, greater capacity was needed and, after much deliberation, it was concluded that extending the Jubilee Line to East London was the most appropriate solution. Maunsell designed not only the line, with the extensive tunnelling involved, but also the impressive new Westminster station. As the deepest and most complex excavation in the UK at the time, this posed an exceptional engineering challenge. A key member of the Maunsell team was Anthony Umney whose expertise in the project management, design and construction of tunnels and underground railways was invaluable. His concept for Westminster station was executed by a team led by Richard Hankin. The open box construction, with the excavation propped by solid steel struts, produced a remarkable design solution acknowledged as the most remarkable of the project's many significant civil engineering achievements. On the Jubilee Line extension, where a new interchange had to be created, not only had the new Jubilee Line platforms to be added but the existing platforms serving other

Maunsell designed and supervised the construction of the extension of London Underground's Jubilee Line from Green Park to Waterloo, including the new Westminster Station shown here. Work began in 1993 and the extension was opened in 1999. (Photograph by courtesy of E C Dixon.)

lines had to be lowered to accommodate the foundations of Portcullis House, the new offices being built above the station for Members of Parliament. Work began at the end of 1993 and the £3.5 billion award-winning extension was opened at the end of 1999 in time for the line to service the controversial Millennium Dome at Greenwich. The team responsible for the Jubilee Line project later worked on the design of the Copenhagen Metro.

In connection with the celebration of the Millennium, the UK firm had been seeking funding to implement the Globorama project. Globorama highlighted the futuristic thinking within the firm. It was an entirely new international communications concept that involved the erection of an electronic world observatory in Greenwich in London. The intention was to link this to outposts across the world, conveying events as they happened. While this reflected the firm's creativity and innovation, it failed to win the grant needed from the Millennium Commission to turn the concept into reality.

At the same time as the Jubilee Line extension, Maunsell was helping to refurbish the ageing Central Line, where the firm's Wriggle program was employed. As a result of the DLR and the Jubilee Line extension, the firm was appointed in 1996, through a British consortium of contractors, to design and supervise the construction of the new Copenhagen Metro. Another automated light rail system, the first section was opened in 2002 with scheduled completion in 2007. From 1996 the UK firm also worked on the design of Singapore's Light Rail Transit System through another international consortium.

In an era of increasing fee competition, Maunsell was also seeking to develop a reputation for providing expert strategic advice. Perhaps the most notable example of this came in 1993 when the firm was appointed to advise the Department of Transport on all engineering and related issues involved in the selection of a private sector company to own and operate the Channel Tunnel Rail Link from London to the Channel Tunnel.

In 1992 Ted Jenkins, after some years as joint managing director with David Hook, became managing director on the latter's retirement. He was an enthusiastic engineer and a dutiful and diligent, but much less enthusiastic, manager. When he left to take up the chairmanship of GMIL in 1993, Peter Jarvis, who had been with Maunsell since 1976, was appointed chief executive of the UK firm. When Jarvis resigned four years later, after disagreements over the international development of the Group, Peter Head replaced him. This came at a difficult time for the UK firm when structural changes made in the early 1990s were being reversed and the various individual Maunsell businesses in the UK were absorbed into one new company, Maunsell Ltd. It did not help that the strong partnership culture that survived within the firm was not suited to the increasingly competitive and commercial nature of the UK market.

It was from the UK that Maunsell's business in the Middle East was managed from the 1970s until the mid-1990s. The firm re-established a major presence in the Emirates in the late 1980s. Attempts were also made to find work in other parts of the Middle East but political instability proved to be a major obstacle. Shakir Al-Kubaisi made several abortive visits to the Lebanon – on one occasion he arrived to discover that the hotel he had booked had been destroyed by missiles – but after the conclusion of the civil war the firm did secure one major contract in the late 1990s. This was to check the design and documentation for the Beirut Seafront, one of the biggest seawalls in the world, part of an enormous scheme to reclaim from the sea 180 hectares to add to the historic commercial and financial centre of Beirut, which had been devastated by the war.

The breakthrough for Maunsell in the Middle East came when Shakir Al-Kubaisi, who travelled regularly throughout the region, called without an invitation on Dubai's chief engineer. His timing was impeccable. The state was just putting out to tender a scheme to increase the capacity of Dubai's dhow wharfage. Maunsell was invited to tender for the design. In association with a US

Maunsell designed and supervised the construction of the dhow wharfage in Dubai, completed in 1993, which was the catalyst for the firm's expansion in the Emirates.

architect, the firm devised an ingenious scheme that proposed four times more capacity than any other submission. Maunsell won the design competition and was also awarded the contract to supervise the construction of the scheme. Work was completed in 1993 and was the catalyst for the firm's rapid growth in Dubai. The firm opened a permanent office, recruited and trained local staff and succeeded in winning more work, not only in Dubai but in neighbouring states such as Qatar and Abu Dhabi. Most of the work was in the field of transportation where the Middle East operation designed and supervised the construction of many urban roads schemes. The operation was also involved in many other interesting projects for a variety of clients, public and private. Among these projects was the cricket stadium in Abu Dhabi for the Adu Dhabi Cricket Council. The strong presence established by Balfour in Al Ain from the 1970s onwards also boosted Maunsell's progress. Balfour established itself as the leading environmental consultant in the area and was

responsible for major water and sewerage projects. The most important of these was the Taweelah water transmission pipelines, with a capacity of more than 80 million gallons of desalinated water per day transmitted a distance of over 150 kilometres. Increasingly reliant on its own local staff and resources, it was decided in 1994 that the Middle East operation should become one of five separate regions (UK/Europe, Australia, Hong Kong/China, Middle East and Sout East Asia) with its own chief executive. Before the end of the decade, under the leadership of Shakir Al-Kubaisi, the Middle East Region was employing some 300 staff.

The 15,000 capacity cricket stadium in Abu Dhabi. Maunsell carried out the structural and services designs.

Although the firm in the UK was involved in many major projects throughout this period, the difficult economic climate, among other factors, produced inconsistent and often disappointing financial results. Although the firm was working on projects throughout Europe and the rest of the world, its base within the UK remained much less secure.

This urban interchange at Al Ain was one of many in the region designed and supervised by Maunsell Middle East.

From Strength to Strength in Hong Kong

Hong Kong remained the strongest part of the Group. In 1990, with 900 employees, it was already the largest consulting engineering firm in South East Asia. With more than 2,000 employees by the end of the decade, it enjoyed an enviable growth record. The firm's substantial workload insulated it for several years from the impact of the collapse of the Asian economy although this was eventually felt early in the new millennium. Francis Bong handed over as chief executive to Tony Shum in 1999 when he became chairman. Shum, who joined the firm in 1977, had worked on the New Towns, on highway projects in Hong Kong and China, had taken over the firm's Environmental Engineering Group in 1993 and then chaired Maunsell Structural Consultants Ltd.

Hong Kong's success during the 1990's did not depend upon the firm's established reputation in highways and transportation, although this still made up an important part of the firm's work. Among such projects Maunsell designed the 4 kilometre long Tate's Cairn road tunnel, the longest in Hong Kong, opened in 1991, and the 4 kilometre long Tai Lam tunnel, completed in 1998. But the firm also diversified into new areas. As the firm expanded, quality assurance and diversification became important, the

Maunsell developed a high reputation for the design of tunnels. This is the entrance to the Tate's Cairn road tunnel, completed in 1991.

former to minimise errors in a larger organisation, the latter so that a downturn in one sector could be matched by an upturn in another. In 1993 Richard Garrett became the Hong Kong office's first Quality Director, leading the process which achieved for the firm the ISO 9000 International Quality Standard certificate to match the rest of the Group.

Diversification was achieved in a variety of ways. An arrangement was reached in 1990 with Taywood Engineering for the maintenance and repair of concrete structures. Although this relationship was short-lived, Maunsell eventually took over the staff and further developed the business. This also happened with another joint venture, Crow Maunsell, formed in 1988 with T W Crow Associates of Sydney, for project management, which was absorbed within Maunsell in 2001. The firm made the most of Balfour's expertise, with Balfour winning the contract for the sewerage master plan study for a large part of Hong Kong in 1990. Once again Balfour's activities were merged into Maunsell in 1994 as the Environmental Engineering Group. Later, after Maunsell merged with AECOM, these activities were strengthened with the help of the Americans, once again illustrating the firm's ethos of exporting knowledge and skills.

The Building Engineering Group, on the other hand, strengthened its own identity. Raymond Ho, who had managed the BEG, left the firm after 20 years in 1993. He was awarded the MBE (Member of the Order of the British Empire) for services to engineering. After his departure, George Gillot took over the management of the group, which, within a year, was employing 100 engineers and support staff and was managing 69 projects. He was a brilliant structural engineer, with a flair for marketing, who got on well with clients and architects alike. Under his stewardship, which lasted until his death in 2001, the BEG continued to make progress. In 1999, in order to create a more distinctive identity for this significant part of the firm, the BEG became Maunsell Structural Consultants Ltd.

The BEG had been the spearhead of Maunsell's strengthening presence in China. In the early 1990s there was a property boom in China's cities, including Guangdong, Shanghai and Beijing. The BEG was responsible for designing and developing a number of prestigious buildings, including the Sky Central Plaza Building in Guangzhou and the Shun Hing Plaza in Shenzen, both over 300 metres high. The boom was short-lived, the Chinese government taking action to dampen an overheated economy in the mid-1990s and many projects were shelved. But Maunsell never lost money and maintained an important number of contacts.

Maunsell targeted its limited resources on the coastal areas, which it had identified as the key part of a huge market. The firm had already formed Maunsell (China) Engineering Services and become the first foreign consulting engineer to open an office in China. This was one of many advantages Maunsell enjoyed over its rivals as the Chinese government progressively opened up the economy. The firm also embarked, as it had in other parts of the world, on a programme of recruiting and training local engineers. With Shanghai United Engineering Consulting

Corporation, another joint company, Shanghai Maunsell Engineering Consultants Ltd (SMEC), was created in 1992. Another, the Jiangsu Maunsell Engineering Consultants & Supervision Co Ltd (JMECS), with an office in Nanjing, was formed in 1996. Through SMEC and JMECS, a wide variety of schemes were undertaken, including the Jiangmen Bridge in Guangdong, the Palace Hotel in Beijing, the Tianyu Urban Development in Shanghai and the Guangzhou to Zhuhai (East Line) expressway. The strong relationship Maunsell had formed with the major Japanese contractor, Kumagai Gumi, in Hong Kong also bore fruit in China with projects such as a major development on Hainan Island.

In Hong Kong the most important project for Maunsell during the 1990s was undoubtedly the master plan for the new international airport at Chek Lap Kok, followed by the project to form the land on which it was built. Maunsell was initially appointed in 1990 with Greiner International of the US to prepare the master plan for the airport. It was a massive project. The airport was to be built on an artificial island of 1248 hectares, of which over 900 were reclaimed from the sea, using material from the island of Chek Lap

Maunsell was jointly responsible for the master plan for Hong Kong's new international airport at Chek Lap Kok, completed in 1998, and went on to design the reclamation that formed the site.

Kok as well as sand dredged from the sea. The dredging of soft marine mud prior to replacement with marine sand involved 40 per cent of the world's dredging fleet. The whole airport took six years to build, cost $20 billion and was opened in July 1998.

The airport had been hugely controversial, causing tension between China and the UK in the run-up to the handover of the Colony in 1997, with the Chinese government accusing the UK of using the airport development to bleed Hong Kong's finances dry. China eventually became more enthusiastic and gave consent for the project to proceed, but by then work had been delayed so long that the airport was be opened only after the handover had taken place. The project included a series of related infrastructure schemes and Maunsell was involved in several of these. For example, one was the 2 kilometre long third road crossing of Hong Kong's Harbour, known as the Western Harbour Crossing, which Maunsell designed in 1993. The first six lane road tunnel in Hong Kong, it was opened in 1997.

Another project where Maunsell excelled was the Kap Shui Mun Bridge. This cable-stayed

Maunsell was involved with the design of Hong Kong's Kap Shui Mun Bridge. Completed in 1997, it is the world's longest cable-stayed bridge carrying both road and rail.

bridge had been designed for the contractor, but the design engineer and the contractor had parted company before the work had been completed. At short notice Maunsell took over the project and the contractor later commented that without Maunsell he doubted if the job would have been finished. Maunsell was also appointed for the Tsing Lung Bridge linking Lantau Island with the New Territories. This structure, a major suspension bridge, will have the world's third longest span when completed. It features the latest technology of twin shallow streamlined boxes spaced apart to optimise their performance under typhoon wind conditions.

Although prospects for future work in Hong Kong seemed bright as the decade drew to a close, there were signs that the good times were drawing to an end. Fee competition was eroding margins while clients were becoming more eager to find someone to blame if a project did not make perfect progress. Maunsell, however, was able to benefit from its pursuit of diversification, ensuring that a decline in one sector was often counter-balanced by an increase in another. This left the firm well-placed to carry Guy Maunsell's ideals into another century.

The Group at a Crossroads

By the late 1990s the Maunsell Group was the third largest transportation engineering consultancy in the world. After the retirement of Ted Jenkins in 1996, the Group appointed its first non-executive chairman. This was Sir Wilfred Newton who had been a non-executive director since 1995. Maunsell's links with Newton went back to the MTR in Hong Kong, which had been completed while Newton was in charge. Newton had then returned to the UK to oversee London Transport as chairman and had been an enthusiastic supporter of the Jubilee Line extension. He was a persuasive and coherent advocate of the process of consolidation and did much to win over those who still harboured doubts. When he stepped down in 1998, his place was taken by John Downer with David Odgers assuming the role of Group Chief Executive.

Between 1990 and 1999 the Group's annual revenues had almost doubled, reaching $230m, of which 70 per cent came from transportation. This had been achieved without a commensurate increase in staff, which now numbered 3,000, thanks to the effective use of modern design and information technology. Yet net earnings of some $7m had remained unchanged for three years. David Odgers pointed out to his GMIL colleagues that Maunsell had reached a plateau. Organic growth was still possible in Europe, Asia and Australia but it would be limited. The prospects for long-term growth from Hong Kong were good but with diminishing returns. North America was still a barren land for the firm, deterred from entering by the scale of litigation prevalent in the USA. The obstacle in South America was language, in Africa, corruption.

Odgers pinpointed several reasons for this situation. The international marketplace was becoming more and more competitive. The relationship between client and consultant was fundamentally changing. It was difficult, in an era when the lowest price for a tender was accepted regardless of other considerations, to convince clients that value for money came from retaining reputable consultants throughout a project. Fee competition reduced the scope of the service offered by the consultant, which produced in turn a rise in litigation between consultant and client and the demise of long-established and respected firms. The type of contract that had almost broken the back of the Australian firm in the late 1980s was increasingly favoured by clients. Requests from clients for consultants to enter into equity partnerships had obvious advantages for the former. For the latter, the risks were also obvious. For Maunsell, in addition, its existing structure, which paid out profits in dividends in order to fund the next generation of shareholders but therefore failed to accumulate capital, made it very difficult to accept such requests.

The trend towards Design & Construct (D&C) and similar types of contract was also changing the relationship between consulting engineer and contractor. D&C contracts confined the client's consultant to defining the project, leaving the contractor's consultant to draw up the details or provide an alternative design. Maunsell found that several difficulties flowed from this type of contract. Firstly, the consulting engineer working for the contractor shared the pressures of time and money under which the contractor was working. Innovative or first-rate designs were rarely produced under these constraints. Secondly, the tension between consulting engineer and contractor was exacerbated when construction began since the site team were under even greater pressures of time and cost and constantly demanded revisions to the original designs without any increase in fees. As a result, there was much greater scope for litigation and the firm found its projected margins being squeezed, with all the consequences this had for cash flow. Ironically, Maunsell, which had done so much since its foundation to improve the relationship between consulting engineer and contractor, found that contractors often had very little respect for the consulting engineer, now usually stripped of his influence to decide which contractor should win the tender. John Downer remembered a hoarding for the Jubilee Line extension that listed Maunsell merely as 'design sub-contractors'.

The difficulties were so great that Maunsell even produced a manual specifically for D&C contracts. Even so, the learning process was painful. The Singapore Light Rail Transit project was a case in point. A report prepared on the project in 1997 noted the absence within the firm of an appropriate risk assessment and management culture. The report continued that 'our only recourse is to change our style of working, since the contractors will predominantly drive D&C work and they will not change to suit us. We must learn more about the construction process and respond to it. We must learn about risk management for the contractor and for ourselves. We must view project completion as the real end of the job – not just the completion of the design period. We must train a new generation of engineers to carry new work paradigms forward. The changes that are required are painful, however, the pain from not resolving our new position in the industry will be even worse.'

As early as 1992 the GMIL board had noted the trend for consulting engineers to turn into 'technical contractors'. By then, because of under-capitalisation resulting from fee competition, half of the leading consulting engineering practices in the UK had already either been absorbed by US firms or undergone drastic structural change. It was hardly surprising at this time that the UK firm – with the Australian firm – should favour growth through acquisition in order to protect themselves from similar fates as a result of being too small to compete effectively in their own markets. The Hong Kong firm, on the other hand, was not in favour of accomplishing this by taking on burdensome debt. In fact, the revival of the Australian firm made it a major player within its home market, an achievement Maunsell in the UK had been unable to emulate.

But Maunsell, hindered by its corporate structure, seemed unsure how best to proceed. In the summer of 1995 it was courted by two firms interested in an international merger, one Dutch, the other Canadian. The Dutch firm was Grontmij, with whom the UK firm had forged a European partnership, but the Group felt any merger with Grontmij would focus too much on Europe and also believed that the way in which Grontmij operated was not compatible with the Maunsell ethos.

The Canadian firm was a recently formed industrial conglomerate called the Cedar Group with offices in Montreal. One of Cedar's companies was Dominion Bridge Inc, which had employed John Laurie four decades earlier. The GMIL board initially believed the Cedar approach was worth investigating since it seemed as if it would create a global business, provide opportunities in North America and not interfere with the management of Maunsell. John Downer and Francis Bong travelled to Canada to meet the Cedar management but it then became obvious that any merger with Cedar would result in the loss of Maunsell's identity and independence.

The Cedar episode had concentrated the minds of GMIL board members on the future development of the Maunsell Group. It now seemed clear that the Group really had only two options. It could become a highly specialised but relatively small niche business; or it could develop as a major all-round provider of professional engineering services on a global scale. The trend of recent years had shown that there was no place for the medium-sized firm – if Maunsell stood still, it would disappear.

Two years later, a more serious merger attempt was made by the firm. Maunsell and Kennedy & Donkin had already been working together. Maunsell was attracted by Kennedy & Donkin's track record in rail engineering, its reputation in the power sector and its strength in electrical and mechanical services. Previously, to offer the all-round service so many more clients were demanding, Maunsell had had to take part in projects jointly with other consultants who possessed the skills Maunsell lacked. This was never a very satisfactory arrangement, most such relationships lasted only as long the project concerned and the exceptions, such as the partnership with Parsons Brinckerhoff, ultimately failed because of the incompatibility between the two organisations.

Maunsell was invited by Kennedy & Donkin's management to participate in the buyout of the company from its parent, Waste Management Inc, with the possibility of acquiring total ownership. But this drew opposition from Maunsell in the UK. While the UK firm needed an alliance with a major partner to boost its position in the market, it was not convinced for a variety of reasons that the merger with this particular partner would work. In any case, for reasons linked to the strategy of Kennedy & Donkin's parent company, the original proposition was not possible.

Twice in two years the Group had seriously considered a merger to create a firm with a global presence in engineering consultancy. Yet shortly after the debate over Kennedy & Donkin, Maunsell's strategy paper for 1997-2001 stated that the firm wanted neither to cede control through the introduction of external ownership nor to seek a merger with a global firm. Instead, the Group would seek acquisitions to achieve regional expansion or obtain new skills.

Under the existing structure of the Group, this was not possible. As David Odgers pointed out to the GMIL board during his first year as chief executive, the Group, although amply equipped with talented engineers, a wide range of skills and an outstanding reputation, simply did not have the financial resources to expand on the scale it needed. Yet the companies achieving the strongest growth in Maunsell's sector were those who did so by acquisition, investing in new markets, developing new services and products, creating genuinely global professional services consultancies. His analysis increased the pressure on all parties to complete the consolidation of Maunsell to secure the future of the international business.

Part 5
1999 Onwards

AECOM

In May 1999, while the journey towards consolidation was continuing to proceed slowly, David Odgers received a telephone call in the Maunsell group head office in London. As he recalled, 'good fortune struck'. The call was from an intermediary acting on behalf of Dick Newman, the chief executive of a US group called AECOM.

AECOM came into being as the result of a management and employee buyout of the portfolio of long-established architectural, engineering and program management businesses belonging to Ashland Oil Inc. The buyout was completed in April 1990. Under the dynamic leadership of Dick Newman, AECOM had grown rapidly as a design and engineering business. By the late 1990s, AECOM had repaid the debt outstanding to its former parent and had created in the USA a diverse business offering a comprehensive range of services, which dominated both the geographic areas where it was located and the service sectors in which it operated. AECOM had increased its turnover from $300m in 1990 to $950m in 1999. But more than 80 per cent of this revenue came from the USA. The next step of AECOM's strategy was to become a global business. To fulfil this objective, AECOM was searching for a suitable international partner, preferably located in the UK and with a strong presence in the Asian market.

Odgers and Newman met over lunch in London and quickly realised that each business could benefit from the other. After a second meeting later the same month, both men agreed that a merger should be sought. The two businesses had much in common. AECOM wanted to share in Maunsell's international presence outside the USA; Maunsell wanted a partner to provide opportunities in North America. Maunsell had skills that AECOM sought and AECOM had skills Maunsell sought. AECOM appreciated the success Maunsell had had in understanding local and regional cultures, an essential skill in building a global presence. AECOM's constituent companies were all allowed to operate independently while enjoying the strong strategic and financial backing of the group. This philosophy of mutual dependence had been practised by Maunsell for decades. And both AECOM and Maunsell were ambitious to become a major global business. For Maunsell, perhaps the greatest attraction of AECOM was the latter's ability to fund future acquisitions. So, when Dick Newman eventually made his presentation to the GMIL board in Brisbane in May 1999, he was asked, 'Are you sure you're not a Maunsell man'. John Downer, who had been sceptical, was won over. His initial reaction had been that AECOM was 'a stable full of horses'; he realised that AECOM's 'stable was full of thoroughbreds'.

Francis Bong recollected that the GMIL board considered AECOM's approach in terms of the impact it would have, firstly, on the firm, secondly, on staff, and, thirdly, on shareholders. The benefits to the firm were obvious, particularly as AECOM had emphasised that Maunsell would operate under its own name outside North and South America and would also take over the existing operations of AECOM companies in the rest of the world. For staff, there would be increased worldwide opportunities within a larger business. (Subsequently not a single member of staff left as a result of the merger.) For the shareholders, the price was fair and it solved the thorny issue of consolidation.

The only outstanding issue was how the three principal groups of shareholders, in the UK, Australia and Hong Kong, would divide the proceeds. By November 1999 they had still not managed to reach an agreement. It was consolidation all over again. So David Odgers met Peter Head, Francis Bong and Nigel Robinson in London and insisted they shut themselves into a room until they came out with an agreement. They emerged an hour and a half later with the deal done. On 18 April 2000, less than twelve months after Dick Newman's first telephone call, the merger was finally concluded. For those who had been promoting the merger, it was particularly satisfying that every single shareholder voted in favour.

The merger has transformed Maunsell and AECOM. From total revenues of nearly a billion dollars and a staff of 11,000 in 2000, AECOM achieved more than $2 billion dollars in revenues and employed 19,000 staff in 2005. Maunsell's difficulties in devising a more effective management approach were swept aside by AECOM's dynamic corporate culture and the leadership example set by its executives. Several Maunsell executives, including John Downer, Francis Bong, David Odgers, Tony Shum and Nigel Robinson, sat either on AECOM's main board, its executive board or both.

Through AECOM's financial strength, combined with its expertise in mergers and acquisitions, Maunsell has continued to expand in every part of the world. In Australasia, for instance, the firm acquired Meritec, the third largest consultant in New Zealand, in 2002. Founded in 1918, with offices in Auckland, Christchurch, Hamilton and Wellington, Meritec gave Maunsell a presence in New Zealand for the first time. In 2004 Maunsell in Australia entered the building services sector when Bassett Consulting Engineers, founded in 1924 and the country's leading electrical and mechanical services consultancy, joined the group. The firm has also increased its stake in its Malaysian and Thai associate firms. In 2001, Nigel Robinson's previous experience in the Middle East led to him being given responsibility for operations in the United Arab Emirates and Qatar.

In the UK Maunsell had been underperforming for some time and failing to make any inroads in the market, although internationally it had continued to carry out a series of major projects and to provide valuable support to other parts of the organisation. So, as soon as the AECOM-Maunsell merger was completed, Newman and Odgers approached the well-known UK consultancy, Oscar Faber, with a view to merging Maunsell's UK business with Faber. The eponymous founder of Oscar Faber, a contemporary of Guy Maunsell, had made his name through significant advances in reinforced concrete technology and had served, like David Lee, as President of the Institution of Structural Engineers. When Faber became part of AECOM at the end of 2001, it employed 1200 staff and was particularly strong in buildings and transport planning. These were significant markets in which the Maunsell in the UK had never had a significant presence. The new entity, Faber-Maunsell, created a firm that was much more than the sum of its two parts, with complementary strengths in buildings, transportation engineering and planning, and environmental engineering and management. Ken Dalton, the chief executive of the new firm, who came from Faber, joined the AECOM executive board. The merger created a business in the UK that offered a full range of services over a wide geographical area. Operating within a tighter and more demanding management regime, the merged firm also had the capability of producing a consistent financial performance.

The Maunsell Heritage

Maunsell is now stronger within AECOM than it ever has been. The determination of the firm to maintain its name and independence, an objective recognised and accepted by AECOM, stems from the lasting influence of Guy Maunsell and the development over 50 years of the vision he set out. Revered in the firm by those who met him and many of those who never did, his founding principles have been evident in the expansion of Maunsell around the world.

Integrity has governed Maunsell's activities wherever the firm has worked. The firm has turned down opportunities where they were accompanied by the need to make unacceptable compromises. Clients have come to respect the firm for offering professional opinions based on the facts rather than on what clients want to hear. This reputation has remained intact despite all the changes that have altered the profession over the years. And the commercial approach that has been so crucial to Maunsell's international development has never compromised the firm's professional integrity.

Fairness towards the client has been matched by fairness towards staff and contractors. It is an all-inclusive philosophy that has turned Maunsell into one of the world's top civil engineering, planning and management consultancies and made it one of the first choices for aspiring young professionals.

Fairness and inclusion have also produced a firm where staff are properly remunerated, where they are given every encouragement to develop their skills, and where their talents are recognised in every part of the world where Maunsell operates. So the Australian firm, founded by expatriates from the UK, is now run by Australians; the Hong Kong firm, begun by an Australian, is run by the local Chinese; and, as Maunsell continues to expand in other parts of the world, the tradition of developing local staff for leadership positions continues.

A practical approach towards design and construction has always been an integral part of the firm. From the Narrows Bridge to the Second Severn Crossing, from the Hammersmith Flyover to Hong Kong's expressways and Australia's modern tollways, from the Western Australia Standard Gauge Project to the Copenhagen Metro, Maunsell has distinguished itself by an understanding of what works best in practice.

This practical approach has been accompanied by a creativity, a flair, an inventiveness that has not only produced designs of supreme elegance, but has also led to innovative techniques benefiting client and contractor. Some of the most beautiful modern bridges have been designed by the firm, from Gladesville in Australia to My Thuan in Vietnam, Benjamin Shears in Singapore to the Second Severn Crossing in England; while some of the world's major infrastructure projects, such as Hong Kong's international airport, the Kwai Chung container port and London's Jubilee Line extension, have been constructed using new ideas developed by teams of Maunsell engineers.

Guy Maunsell always wanted every part of the firm to remain in touch with each other, to communicate clearly with each other, never to become detached and separate. One of the strongest of all the firm's attributes has been a desire for unity, not for its own sake, but to strengthen the firm through mutual support and co-operation. This has been a springboard to success, not just in individual projects, but in establishing Maunsell in new parts of the world. Where the tensions of international growth might have led some firms to stagnate or disintegrate, unity, combined with transparency, has allowed the firm to remain intact and, through open if painful discussion, reach agreement on the way forward.

Guy Maunsell's principles have resonated with many cultures and nationalities and the quality of the Maunsell culture, founded on absolute respect for people, has attracted professionals of the highest calibre. Through them, the firm has always been conscious of the need for technical excellence that, combined with a commercial awareness, has seen the firm emerge as a leading global business when so many rivals have fallen by the wayside. Recently, in Australia, John Downer, whose services to engineering were recognised by the award of the AM (Member of the Order of Australia) in 2001, spoke to a large group of graduates who had only just joined the firm – several later asked if they could meet him to talk about Maunsell in more depth. Fifty years after Guy Maunsell founded the firm, there is still a great pride and interest in the Maunsell name and Maunsell heritage, a demonstration of a great engineer's continuing relevance.

Index

Appendix I
Guy Maunsell's Philosophy

It is recognised that the first duty of the partnership is to serve the interests of the clients. In the first place, it will not be the policy of this partnership to extract fees of greater value than the services rendered, it will, on the contrary, be our policy whenever possible to render services greatly in excess of what we get paid.

Consulting Civil Engineers in the past have as a rule not concerned themselves very much with the way in which works are carried out, but we intend to adopt a different attitude. It will be our endeavour when we are designing works at the same time to plan the way in which those works are to be put into execution. Our reason for this is because we have found by experience that when design and planning of construction go hand in hand, the cost of the work and the time taken to perform it can be accurately forecast, but when design and planning are divorced, estimated cost and estimated times for construction are liable to be greatly exceeded, involving clients or contractors, or both, in heavy loss. In all cases of difficult or heavy civil engineering work, we shall therefore attempt to plan the carrying out at the same time as we are designing it, and we shall give contractors tendering for the work access to our ideas. In this way we believe we can render an important service to our clients.

Next, as regards our attitude to contractors, we intend to treat these people with sympathy and consideration, giving to them the maximum degree of help compatible with our clients' interests.

In the matter of internal relationships between partners, associates and employees, our basic idea is to deal openly and fairly. We recognise the principle that every person engaged in or by our organisation is entitled to receive, year by year, a fair share of any benefits, financial gain, or kudos which has resulted from the efforts of that person. Not only do we partners recognise the principle, but by giving practical application to it we shall seek to bring realisation of it to the minds of those associated with or employed by us.

We recognise that the policy here stated may, to some extent, involve us in the abandonment of excessive secrecy as to the nature and extent of our trading results.

We recognise also that the policy will prevent the creation of too sharp a line of demarcation between partners and others.

It is intended that every individual (including partners) actively engaged in the business of the Firm shall receive basic remuneration assessed on his current value in the labour market, and that in addition to this, if trading results permit, every person shall receive a proportion of profits graded according to his basic remuneration, plus a further slice of profits in cases of special merit.

It is not our intention that profits earned by the partnership shall (beyond the accumulation of a necessary reserve fund) be hidden away for the ultimate enrichment of partners, but distributed.

As regards the management of the partnership affairs, we consider it to be of great importance that the activities of the several partners, their associates, consultants, and assistants shall be co-ordinated and remain under centralised control and shall not be allowed to disperse or separate out into water-tight compartments.

With this in view, we propose to place the general directions of the affairs at any and every time under the personal control of one of the partners selected by the vote of his co-partners.

G. A. Maunsell – 1955

Appendix II
Maunsell Timeline

Date	Guy Maunsell's Life	Key Corporate Events	Key Projects	World & Other Events	Date
1828				ICE founded	1828
1884	Birth of Guy Maunsell				1884
1885				General Gordon murdered at Khartoum	1885
1901				Death of Queen Victoria	1901
1904				Prestressed concrete invented	1904
1906				San Francisco earthquake	1906
1907	In Switzerland			Picasso introduces Cubism	1907
1908	Agent for concrete contracting firm			Henry Ford launches the Model T	1908
1909	Working at Rosyth naval dockyard			Robert Peary reaches the North Pole	1909
1914				First World War begins	1914
1917	Serving in France			Russian Revolution	1917
1918	Designs concrete ships			First World War Peace declared	1918
1919	Proposes Channel Tunnel				1919
1927				Lindbergh flies the Atlantic	1927
1929				Wall Street Crash	1929
1931	Supervises widening of Putney Bridge				1931
1932				Sydney Harbour Bridge opened	1932
1933				Hitler becomes Chancellor	1933
1934	Supervises building of Storstrom Bridge				1934
1935	Becomes consulting civil engineer				1935
1937	Practising as G A Maunsell, Consulting Engineer				1937
1938	Working on Menai Straits Bridge			Munich Agreement	1938
1939				Second World War begins	1939
1940	Proposes floating harbour			Churchill becomes British Prime Minister	1940
1940	Proposes naval sea fort			Dunkirk evacuated	1940
1941				USA enters the war	1941

Date	Guy Maunsell's Life	Key Corporate Events	Key Projects	World & Other Events	Date
1942	First naval and army sea forts			Battle of El Alamein	1942
1943	Proposes floating concrete docks			Mussolini overthrown	1943
1944		Posford becomes partner		D Day Landings	1944
1945		Pavry becomes partner		End of the war in Europe & Asia	1945
1948				Berlin Airlift	1948
1949		Pavry becomes partner		Mao Tse Tung takes over in China	1949
1950				Korean War	1950
1955		G Maunsell & Partners formed	Floating sea boring units	Peron overthrown in Argentina	1955
1957		John Baxter, Managing Partner, UK		Russia launches first earth satellite	1957
1957		Miles Birkett in charge of Australian office			1957
1958		Maunsell working in Iraq	Oyster Creek Bridge, The Gambia, & 'Gambia' piles	Revolution in Iraq	1958
1959	Retires from partnershuip		Canberra	Castro takes over in Cuba	1959
1960			Narrows Bridge, Perth	Kennedy becomes President of the USA	1960
1961	Death		Hammersmith Flyover, London	Gagarin makes first space flight	1961
1961			Western Australia Standard Gauge Project		1961
1962			Brumen Bridge, The Gambia	End of French rule in Algeria	1962
1964			Tasman Bridge, Hobart	Harold Wilson becomes British Prime Minister	1964
1964			Gladesville Bridge, Sydney	Opening of the Forth Road Bridge in Scotland	1964
1964			King's Avenue & Commonwealth Avenue Bridges, Canberra		1964
1965		Maunsell & Partners, Australia, formed		Vietnam war begins	1965
1966			Malta naval dockyard	England win the World Cup	1966

Date	Guy Maunsell's Life	Key Corporate Events	Key Projects	World & Other Events	Date
1968			Westway, London, and The Mancunian Way, Manchester	Martin Luther King assassinated	1968
1968			Batman Bridge, Tasmania	Russians invade Czechoslovakia	1968
1969		Short-lived South African operations begin		Maiden flight of Concorde	1969
1969		Maunsell begins operations in Singapore		Death penalty abolished in the UK	1969
1970		Maunsell & Partners Pty Ltd, Australia formed	Captain Cook Memorial Fountain, Canberra		1970
1970		Maunsell Consultants formed	Route 4 Expressway, Hong Kong		1970
1970		Maunsell Consultants Asia formed	First environmental services commission, Australia		1970
1970		Maunsell begins operations in Hong Kong	West Gate Bridge, Melbourne		1970
1971		Sindhu Maunsell Consultants formed in Thailand			1971
1972				Watergate scandal	1972
1973		Maunsell Consultants Ltd incorporated	Sha Tin New Town, Hong Kong	Oil price rises set off world recession	1973
1975		Maunsell re-enters Iraq as Al-Kubaisi & Partner	Adamiyah Bridge, Baghdad		1974
1975			Sembawang dockyard, Singapore	Whitlam's Government dismissed in Australia	1975
1975			Tasman Bridge, Hobart, reconstructed		1975
1976			Temerloh Bridge, Malaysia	Soweto riots in South Africa	1976
1976			Mass Transit Railway, Hong Kong	Israeli raid on Entebbe	1976
1976			Suez Canal Study	Death of Mao Tse Tung	1976
1978			Dampier-Perth LNG Pipeline, Australia	Pope John Paul II elected	1978
1979		Maunsell enters France	Baghdad International Airport, Iraq	Margaret Thatcher becomes British Prime Minister	1979

Date	Guy Maunsell's Life	Key Corporate Events	Key Projects	World & Other Events	Date
1980		Maunsell Geotechnical Services created in Hong Kong		Ronald Reagan elected President of the United States	1980
1981		Essex RCU sub-unit joins Maunsell in UK	ACCS developed	Marriage of Prince Charles & Lady Diana Spencer	1981
1982			Aberdeen Tunnel, Hong Kong	Falklands War	1982
1983		Maunsell Structural Plastics Ltd formed in UK			1983
1984		Maunsell Holdings Ltd formed	Second Severn Crossing, UK	Sino-British agreement reached on Hong Kong	1984
1984		Maunsell Ltd formed in UK	Docklands Light Railway, London	Indira Ghandi assassinated	1984
1984		G Maunsell & Partners incorporated			1984
1985		Maunsell Consultancy incorporated	Tremie Tube in Australia		1985
1986		G Maunsell & Partners International Ltd formed		Queen signs proclamation giving Australia independence	1986
1988			New Parliament House roads and bridges in Canberra		1988
1988			Kwai Chung container port, Hong Kong	Lockerbie air disaster	1988
1989		Halpern Glick Maunsell formed	National Tennis Centre, Melbourne	Berlin Wall comes down	1989
1989		D Balfour & Sons/CES joins Maunsell			1989
1989		Guy Maunsell International Ltd formed			1989
1990		Guy Maunsell International Services Ltd formed	Chek Lap Kok international airport, Hong Kong	Nelson Mandela is freed	1990
1991			Tate's Cairn Tunnel, Hong Kong	The Gulf War	1991
1992		Denis Johnston & Associates joins Maunsell	Aberfeldy ACCS bridge, Scotland	Official end of the Cold War	1992

Date	Guy Maunsell's Life	Key Corporate Events	Key Projects	World & Other Events	Date
1992		Shanghai Maunsell created	M5 Tollway, Sydney		1992
1993			Jubilee Line extension, London		1993
1993			Dubai dhow wharfage		1993
1994		Grontmij joint company created in Europe		Channel Tunnel opened	1994
1995		Maunsell enters Malaysia			1995
1995		Maunsell enters Philippines			1995
1996		Jiangsu Maunsell created	Copenhagen Metro, Denmark		1996
1996			Light Rail Transit System, Singapore		1996
1997			Western Harbour Crossing, Hong Kong	Hong Kong returned to China	1997
1998		Maunsell McIntyre formed	Tai Lam Tunnel, Hong Kong		1998
2000		Maunsell becomes part of AECOM	My Thuan Bridge, Vietnam		2000
2002		Meritec becomes part of Maunsell			2002
2002		FaberMaunsell created in UK			2002
2004		Bassett Consulting Engineers joins Maunsell		Last flight of Concorde	2004
2005		Bullens joins Maunsell in UK			

Among books by the same authors are:

Nigel Watson

The Last Mill on the Esk – 150 years of Papermaking, Scottish Academic Press, 1987

The Bibby Line 1807-1990 – A Story of Booms & Slumps, James & James, 1990

The Celestial Glass Bottle Company – A Short Centenary History of Lax & Shaw Ltd, 1891-1991
     Granta Editions, 1991

Time & Tide Wait for No Man – George Hammond PLC 1767-1992, Granta Editions, 1992

Brown Brothers – A Company History 1871-1996, privately published, 1996

The Story of Christian Salvesen 1846-1996, James & James, 1996

The Story of Airsprung 1870s-1990s, privately published, 1997

The Roots of BSW Timber plc – 150 Years in the Timber Industry, St Matthew's Press, 1998

60 Years of Kangol Quality 1938-1998, privately published, 1998

When the Question is Steam – The Story of Spirax-Sarco, James & James, 2000

In Their Fathers' Footsteps – The story of the James Donaldson Group, St Matthew's Press, 2001

Waste Matters – A History of Cleansing Service Group, James & James, 2002

The Business of Adding Value – A Short History of the Christie Group, Christie Group, 2004

Frank Turner

The Maunsell Sea Forts, Part One, The Sea Forts, ISBN 05924303-0-4, Self published 1994

The Maunsell Sea Forts, Part Two, The Army Forts, ISBN 05924303-1-2, Self Published 1995

The Maunsell Sea Forts, Part Three, The Human Elements, ISBN 05924303-7-1, Self Published 1996

Gravesend Airport in photographs, ISBN 1901132-00-5, Self Published 1997

Maunsell Secret Wartime Proposals (Five Parts Series), Self Published 1997

A Cypriot Airman without Wings, ISBN 1901132-10-2, Self Published 1998

Chatham Built Submarines, ISBN1901132-09-7, Self Published 1999

German Vengeance Weapons (Three Parts Series), Self Published 2004

The Definitive History of the Thames Forts (Seven Parts Series), Self Published 2005